Kingston & the Islands ✓ **W9-CCU-817**

Fuelling
Canada's
Future

EX LIBRIS

Randy Manning

Fuelling Canada's Future

WADE ROWLAND

Macmillan of Canada
1974

© Wade Rowland 1974

All rights reserved. The use of any part of this
publication reproduced, transmitted in any form or by
any means, electronic, mechanical, photocopying,
recording, or otherwise, or stored in a retrieval system,
without the prior consent of the publisher is an
infringement of copyright law.

ISBN: Cloth 0-7705-1215-1
      Paper 0-7705-1201-1

Printed in Canada for
The Macmillan Company of Canada Limited
70 Bond Street, Toronto M5B 1X3

FOR SOME OF THOSE WHO DESERVED BETTER:
Heather, Michael, George, Julia, Tiny, Joy, Carmel,
Robin, Doug, Hope, Susan, Bronwyn, Vince, Maryann,
Sam, Elaine, Ken, Caroline, Eloise, Murray, Carla, Carol . . .
but mostly for Sarah Lea.

Contents

Preface ix

Introduction 1

1. Energy in Perspective 7

2. The Northern Frontier 27

3. The Alberta Tar Sands 62

4. Nuclear Promises 84

5. The Problem of Energy Conservation 116

   Appendix 1: An Approach to Achieving the Steady
   State 137

   Appendix 2: Oil Shale in the United States 139

   Appendix 3: Everything You Ever Wanted to Know About
   Energy in Canada 142

   Selected Bibliography 159

Preface

This book was originally conceived as a series of essays for a new Canadian magazine which, unfortunately, followed in the footsteps of many a predecessor and folded after only one issue had reached the newsstands. I say unfortunately not because it was a good magazine—it wasn't—but because it promised to pay the highest rates for freelance articles such as mine. Moreover, it was willing to publish articles of up to and over ten thousand words in length, while virtually all other Canadian magazines judge the attention span of their readers to extend at maximum to about thirty-five hundred words, and will accept nothing longer. It is pretty difficult for a prose writer to treat any serious topic comprehensively in thirty-five hundred words, which is part of the reason for the generally trivial character of the magazines in this country . . . but that is beside the point.

Only chapter 1 was actually completed before the magazine went under; it was subsequently revised, and the rest of the chapters were written specifically for this book. The introduction appeared in an abridged form in the May 1974 issue of *Chatelaine* magazine, and parts of chapter 1 were published in the *Financial Post*, May 25, 1974.

I would like to thank the engineers at Atomic Energy Canada Limited's Sheridan Park establishment for their patience in explaining to me many of the more arcane details of reactor design and for their frankness in discussing the controversial subject of reactor safety. And I would like to acknowledge the assistance given me by the librarians at Ontario Hydro's excellent research library, where I was allowed to photocopy scientific articles to my heart's content.

W.D.R.

June 1974
Bronte, Ontario

Fuelling
Canada's
Future

Introduction

I have been writing about environmental problems for five or six years now; to anyone who expresses an interest I can show scrapbooks bulging with scores of newspaper stories, a couple of articles reprinted in a paperback anthology, a layman's guide to the major pollution problems in Canada, an ecology book for kids and a book about the historic 1972 U.N. Conference on the Human Environment at Stockholm. And, of course, this present volume of essays.

My attitude to the subject has gone through a number of changes over the years. When I first began to spend most of my time at the Toronto *Telegram* doing what we called "pollution stories," I believed, like my editors and most of my colleagues, that the solution to the problem lay in strictly enforced government regulations prohibiting industrial pollution, and improved municipal garbage and sewage treatment facilities. But as time passed and I began to understand better how widespread and deep-running pollution problems had become, I formed the opinion that what was necessary was a concerted effort to remould our technology to serve our newly seen goal of cleaning up our act and keeping it clean. I became a great admirer of Buckminster Fuller and his theories of "ephemeralization." Basically, Fuller was saying that pollution is waste and waste implies inefficient use of materials; by making our technology operate more efficiently—by designing it to do more work with less in the way of inputs—we can reduce pollution. He argued convincingly that it is completely within our present capabilities to increase the over-all efficiency of world technology by a factor of at least three, to the point where there can at last be "enough of everything to go around." At the same time, environmental damage would automatically be reduced to a more acceptable level. I wrote voluminously and with some enthusiasm about the need to exploit this promise of technology.

There was just one hitch in all of this: the population explosion that will almost certainly have left us with twice the current world population of 3.5 billion within thirty-five years or so. Twice as many people to feed, house, clothe and educate. For a time I was willing to suspend judgment on this issue and, in effect, accept on faith the word of those who were arguing that an efficiently run world could support at least twice the present human population. However, as I continued to research and write I was continually turning up information that made this position seem untenable. The so-called Green Revolution that was supposed to provide everyone on earth with an adequate diet through increased farm mechanization and improved grain strains was simply not working, and in the end even its U.N. sponsors were admitting their profound disappointment. Massive irrigation projects were spreading disease and poisoning land with salt; intensive use of machinery was destroying the natural tilth of land; many of the new crop strains were susceptible to pest infestation; massive use of fertilizers was causing serious water pollution problems; and with the increasing shortages of low-priced petroleum, fuel for machinery was becoming prohibitively expensive and synthetic fertilizer all but unobtainable. Agriculture, then, was one area where a concerted effort had been made to increase world efficiency, and the attempt had fallen far, far short of expectations. I wrote about this in the book I prepared for children, trying to explain how populations grow so much faster than agricultural production can grow, and how we seemed to have lost whatever opportunity we might once have had to balance the two without having to experience massive famines.

Looking at the relationship between food and population got me more involved in the whole area of resource depletion. I tried to describe for the kids what I had come to think of as the paradox of the population explosion: that from the point of view of depletion of non-renewable resources it could be argued that North America and Western Europe were the real areas of over-population in the world. I wrote:

> If you were to calculate the total amount of energy produced by various kinds of machines in Canada and the United States and convert it into human muscular power, you would find that every Cana-

dian and American has the equivalent of about five hundred human "slaves" working for him. All that energy—all that ability to do work —has to come from somewhere: if it doesn't come from real slaves it has to come from raw materials like coal and petroleum. Slowly but surely we are beginning to run out of many of those resources which, once used, cannot be replaced. And the populations of the developed world, though generally smaller than those of the underdeveloped world, are the ones that are mainly responsible.

The United States, for example, has only 6 per cent of the world's population, but uses about a third of the world's yearly production of raw materials. Can you see how, to a country in Asia that is eager to get its share of natural resources so as to give its people a high standard of living, the United States might seem to be overpopulated?

At about this stage the work which laid the foundation for the Club of Rome–MIT report, *The Limits to Growth*, first began to circulate. Studying this material, the first computer-assisted analysis of global food, resources and pollution problems, I began to understand why it was that environmental crises seemed to blossom almost before anyone was aware of their budding. It was so beautifully, so ironically simple. Resource consumption, and therefore waste production and pollution, increase exponentially. That is, they tend to double and redouble at regular intervals over time—intervals that can be predicted if you know the rate of growth. If you plot an exponential growth curve, you find that for a long time it grows deceptively slowly. As the base for each new doubling gets larger, the curve gets steeper. And then it suddenly shoots upward right off the graph. All the information I had access to indicated that in a frightening number of cases of resource depletion and pollution levels we were at that point on the curve where it begins suddenly to go vertical. I began to write about this, to try to share my new understanding with others.

In the summer of 1972 I attended the U.N.-sponsored Stockholm Conference. Being there for two weeks in the midst of all the high-level wheeling and dealing, and writing the book that grew out of that experience, caused another major shift in my point of view. I became aware of the third world's special perspective on environmental problems; of their feeling of the absurdity of getting excited about industrial pollution when they were still unable to provide basic food, shelter and sanitation for their illiterate masses. The issues of air and water pollution, solid waste disposal and so on—all the things I had been writing about at the *Telegram* only a few months earlier—seemed to be almost ludicrously insignificant when compared to the problems of dwindling resources, the food gap and the global maldistribution of wealth and the havoc they were almost certain to wreak on the international diplomatic scene.

A statement made by economist Barbara Ward in a conference preparatory document struck me as being perhaps the best single comment made so far on the environmental crisis:

> We can cheat on morals. We can cheat on politics. We can deceive ourselves with dreams and myths. But there is no monkeying about with DNA or photosynthesis or eutrophication or nuclear fusion or the impact on all living things of excessive radiation—from the sun or the hydrogen bomb. What our incredible scientific breakthroughs of the last century have taught us is that the ultimate energy of the universe both sustains and destroys life and that the mechanisms and balances by which it becomes life-enhancing are fragile and precious beyond our belief. To act without rapacity, to use knowledge with wisdom, to respect interdependence, to operate without hubris and greed are not simply moral imperatives. They are an accurate scientific description of the means of survival.

From time to time over the years I was asked whether or not I was optimistic that our environmental problems could be brought under control in time to avoid major calamity. For a while I used to reply that, yes, there were signs that enough people were becoming aware of the dangers of pollution; that there was reason to believe that things could be brought under control relatively quickly. Later, as I came to understand more of the dynamics of population growth and food production and resource depletion, I became more sceptical. I would tell anyone who asked that while I still thought that it was within our capabilities to solve our pollution problems, I didn't see how we could avoid immense famines and sudden resource shortages and the political disruptions these would inevitably cause. I numbered myself among the pessimists.

Then, one evening I was watching a televised discussion between James Baldwin, the American expatriate writer, and a young New York author. Baldwin said something that made me feel that my pessimism must be phony posturing.

4

"Pessimists are silent," Baldwin said. And I was anything but silent, what with two books behind me and another on the same subject in the works. If I were truly pessimistic I would not be wasting my time trying to inform people about problems they couldn't possibly solve in time.

So I came to accept the idea that, at heart, I was an optimist. When the first indications of the looming world-wide energy crisis began making their appearance in the United States in the summer of 1973, a radio interviewer asked me about the predicted gasoline shortages there. This is what I told him:

> I have great hopes for the energy crisis. . . . It is going to get more and more acute as the summer goes by and they get into winter and increased heating oil demands. And I am hopeful that people will begin to ask why we are running out. Right now they're blaming the oil companies. They're saying it's a conspiracy. To me, that is really just a red herring. The problem is that they are driving too damn many Cadillacs that get eight miles per gallon, and they're building ridiculous houses and office towers that cost a fortune to heat and air condition; they are overlighting them so that they have to air condition to compensate for the extra heat generated by the lights. Those are the kinds of things that have to be looked at. . . . I don't think people realize how rapidly we are running out of a whole list of basic resources. It is going to be quite a chaotic time over the next twenty to twenty-five years as various nations begin to face this problem. Imagine how you would feel if you were a Nigerian and you had just reached the take-off point to sustained development and you found that there were no damned resources left to develop with—not only in terms of the rest of the world, but you find that the resources that were in your own country have been sold off to the rich nations at ridiculously low prices, as the oil was in the Persion Gulf. The Americans in particular are screaming about the Persian Gulf oil prices going up. Well, my God, they've been far too low since day one.

At that time, of course, no one suspected that the Mid-East war and the Arab oil embargo would give us a foretaste of the kind of shortages we wouldn't otherwise have experienced until well into the next decade. What we experienced through the embargo was a kind of dry run for the real crisis to come when, before long, we will have used up all of the world's economically accessible petroleum reserves. And oil is only the first of many raw materials that will be coming into short supply.

It is our reaction to the test case of the current oil shortages that has led me to shift my point of view once again—I suspect for the last time. We are faced with a situation that clearly demands a thoroughgoing, even revolutionary change in our entire approach to resource use, a switch from promoting growth and throughput to an emphasis on stability and preservation of stocks. Our answer has been to ensure that growth and throughput can continue, by suspending hard-won anti-pollution legislation and brushing aside criticism of pipeline and resource exploitation projects and massive new power developments as unimportant in the face of the "need" for more energy. Tragically, one must conclude that President Nixon was voicing the majority sentiment of our own (more discreet) political and economic leaders when he said:

"There are only seven per cent [sic] of the people of the world living in the United States, and we use 30 per cent [33 per cent, in fact] of all the energy. That isn't bad; that is good. That means we are the richest, strongest people in the world. That is why we need so much energy, and may it always be that way."

I read that, and then I re-read what Barbara Ward had to say, and I could almost weep. I have the feeling that I have seen the future and, as they say, it doesn't work. If I continue to write about this subject, it can no longer be with enthusiasm. It can only be with a kind of morbid, compulsive fascination. Baldwin was only partly correct: even the doomed Captain Scott, hopelessly lost on the Antarctic ice cap, noted in his diary the dwindling of his supplies; recorded, one by one, the deaths of his companions, and his own sensations, as the darkness crept in and an heroic adventure ended in tragedy.

1.
Energy in Perspective

The energy crisis is not a short-term problem. It will not go away next spring, or even by 1980, the target date Mr. Nixon set for his impossible dream of short-run energy self-sufficiency in the United States. Moreover, energy supplies are only the first of several crucial non-renewable resources that will be coming into short supply over the next two or three decades. The current energy crisis, an existing problem made only slightly worse by the Arab oil embargo, is a dry run, a pale preview of what the future holds in store for the industrialized world. All the elements of incipient chaos are there, if only in embryonic form: the international political blackmail, the retaliatory threats to cut off food supplies, the chauvinistic calls for self-sufficiency, the "I'm all right, Jack" bloody-mindedness of the resource-rich areas and the angry, indignant reaction of the resource-poor; the cavalier setting aside of hard-won knowledge of the fragility of the human environment as governments move to shelve anti-pollution legislation; the trampling of environmental protection groups in the stampede to push through Arctic pipelines, build dams, rip up scarce grazing land to strip-mine coal and oil shale . . . and on and on.

Much of the heat generated in the current debate over the energy crisis stems from the fact that there are two different ways of looking at the long-term energy situation. To the resource industry, the problem is one of how to get the dwindling reserves out of the ground and to market quickly enough and in large enough volumes to meet a world demand which is expected to double by 1985. The environmentalist, on the other hand, sees the crisis as existing in the possibility that the resource industry will achieve its goal, with all that would mean to an already over-burdened global environment. To put it another way, the question being asked by the resource industry is: "How can we best meet present and forecast demands?" while the question asked by the environmentalist is: "How can we reduce those demands to a level where the environmental consequences of meeting them can be kept to a manageable level?" A third question, closely related to the second, might also be asked: "How can we make our conventional energy reserves last long enough to give us a chance to invent and develop alternate energy sources against that inevitable day of reckoning when conventional supplies are exhausted?"

It is worthwhile examining the widely divergent predictions as to how long known reserves of oil, gas and coal can be expected to last. The confusion arises partly out of the fact that at least three different forecasting methods are being employed. First, there are projections based on "current rates of use." These take note of the amount of a resource being used in the current year and presume that the same amount will be used each year in the future, until reserves are exhausted. Of course, the fact is that as populations continue to grow and become more prosperous the amount consumed of virtually any resource increases year by year. But in the past, this method of prediction of the life expectancy of reserves was nonetheless more realistic than it might seem, since new reserves were being discovered at a rate that equalled or exceeded the amount consumed each year. For every billion barrels of oil used, exploration teams could be counted upon to find at least a billion barrels of new reserves somewhere in the world. The two tended to balance each other out, so that the current rate of use forecast was for a time reasonably accurate. However, in the cases of oil and gas at least, the annual rates of consumption have for some time been considerably higher than the rate of discovery. This is partly because consumption has increased so rapidly and partly because so much of the world's remaining accessible reserves have already been discovered. So forecasts based on current rates of use tend to be wildly optimistic and should be taken with a healthy pinch of salt. Unfortunately, it is precisely this kind of forecast that is most often quoted in the news media.

The most pessimistic of the forecasts one hears are generally based on the predicted rate of growth in use of a resource. These forecasts are most often made by noting the average rate of growth in consumption over a period of years in the recent past and projecting that rate into the future with exponential growth calculations. It can be calculated, for instance, that regardless of current volumes of use, if the rate of growth in consumption is 4 per cent a year, total consumption will double in eighteen years. Or if the rate of growth is 7 per cent a year, total consumption will double in ten years. This continual doubling and re-doubling leads to tremendous explosions in growth if the rate of growth is unchecked.

Thus, to take coal as an example, forecasts based on current rate of use predict that known world reserves (about 50 trillion tons) should last 2,300 years. However, if the second forecasting method, which allows for the rate of growth in yearly consumption (about 4.1 per cent, globally) is used, the predicted life of reserves plummets to just 111 years. Because it seems unlikely that major accessible reserves of coal remain undiscovered, the second prediction must be taken as more accurate than the first, which assumes discoveries will equal consumption each year.

A third method of forecasting was devised by M. King Hubbert, a resources expert at the U.S. Geological Survey. According to Hubbert, consumption trends follow the pattern predicted by the pessimistic rate of growth formula until costs of production increase enough to cause the beginning of a levelling off. When 90 per cent of known reserves have been exhausted, consumption and production start to decline. (If you plot a graph of the rise and fall of consumption based on Hubbert's theory, you wind up with a bell-shaped curve that is known as "Hubbert's pimple.") Hubbert's prediction for the length of time it will take to reach the levelling-off point for coal is about 200 years; 90 per cent of reserves would be exhausted in about 425 years.

Hubbert's predictions and others like them, which make allowance for a levelling-off effect, are probably the most accurate of the three. But it can be argued that, depending on where the levelling-off point is placed, by the time it has been reached the cost of producing more of the resource will have risen so high that consumption will fall off quickly and the effect will be virtually the same as if reserves had been exhausted anyway. The average driver would be no better off for knowing that there is plenty of gasoline available if it cost $20 a gallon.

In view of all of this, predictions for the life of resource reserves should be made only with the utmost caution and with all qualifications clearly stated. Nonetheless, this much can probably be safely said:

• World oil reserves available to us with foreseeable technology (excluding tar sand and oil shale deposits) will be *effectively* exhausted as a viable energy source by the year 2000 or earlier. Even if major new reserves are discovered, this date is unlikely to be altered by more than a very few years unless we begin immediately to cut back on the rate of growth in consumption. The 10-billion-barrel proved reserve discovered at Prudhoe Bay in Alaska (for which we are about to suffer construction of the Trans-Alaska pipeline and a new supertanker route through the treacherous coastal waters off British Columbia) represents a two-year supply for today's U.S. market. The entire proved reserves of the United States, counting Alaska and offshore reserves, amount to only a ten-year supply for the home market even at current rates of use. And those rates are forecast to triple by 2000.

• World natural gas reserves could be effectively exhausted by about the same time if rates of use continue to increase as projected. Even if consumption were immediately frozen at today's level, known and suspected reserves in the United States and Canada would last the North American market less than seventy-five years. They could last less than thirty years if consumption continues increasing as it has in the recent past.

• Coal reserves should hold out well into the next century, even allowing for huge increases in consumption as gas and oil become scarce and coal is used more and more to produce synthetic substitutes.

• As for those vaunted tar sand and oil shale reserves, the Athabaska tar sands hold immense amounts of oil, perhaps as much as a third of total world reserves. Unfortunately only 10 to 15 per cent of it (about 35 billion barrels) is recoverable even at $6 a barrel. As the going price rises, of course, more will be economically recoverable. But how much higher will the price have to go before it becomes worth while to mine and refine more than an additional 5 or 10 per cent? Will that price be within reach of the ordinary consumer? For the moment, at least, it seems likely that we will have moved on to cheaper alternative forms of energy before it ever becomes economically feasible to exploit much more than a quarter of the tar sands' potential. Viewed from this perspective the promise of the sands tends to fade somewhat.

Fortunately, the fossil fuels—gas, oil and coal—are by no means our only sources of energy. There already are a large number of nuclear power plants in operation around the world, and for the future we can look to exploitation of direct solar energy and new forms of nuclear energy, as well as a number of other minor sources. And then, too, there is hydroelectric power (which provides more than 75 per cent of Canada's electricity needs, but only 17 per cent of total consumption in the United States).

The one thing all of these alternative sources of power have in common is their lack of portability. You can't pour any of them into a gas tank and drive off. They are all used to produce electricity which, given the current state of storage battery technology, must in virtually all cases be transported by wire (although scientists are now giving some thought to using electricity to produce liquid and gaseous hydrogen which could be moved by underground pipeline like gas). Each, too, has its own impact on the environment, which also must be considered.

Hydroelectric energy is really just another form of stored solar energy. The solar energy used to evaporate sea water is tapped by storing the water behind dams once it has precipitated and drained into rivers. The dammed water is channelled through turbines which drive electric generators. Like all schemes to trap the sun's power, hydro projects must cope with the fact that solar energy is very diffuse. This means that the machinery for exploiting it tends to cover a lot of territory. A hydro scheme consists of more than just the obvious dams and generating plant; it also includes the water stored behind the dam in artificial lakes, and for that matter, the whole river system behind that.

Hydro is undoubtedly the cleanest source of electric power currently available to us. Whether it is still the cheapest is a matter of controversy, particularly if all the external costs involved in such huge engineering projects as Hydro Quebec's James Bay development and Manitoba's Churchill River diversion are taken into account. Unfortunately, most of these external costs are difficult to calculate. What value, for instance, should be assigned to the loss of a way of life for thousands of Indians who hunt and trap in the James Bay area? What is the cost to us of the sacrifice of a fundamental tenet of democracy—the sacredness of minority rights—when our courts rule that the majority's desire for more energy is of paramount importance? What price should be assigned to the unique waterfowl breeding areas in the Churchill River that will be submerged by damming? What loss is entailed in turning a beautiful river gorge into a large, torpid, artificial lake? And there are other costs downstream from the dam where the controlled outflow reduces strong seasonal fluctuations in water volumes and temperature; spring freshets are diminished with the result that the winter ice cover on the river remains longer. This means that the date of germination and reproduction of life in the river valley and adjacent areas can be seriously delayed. Conditions in the river estuary may also be seriously affected with sea ice remaining inshore longer and marine food supplies being thereby altered. Damming of river waters allows suspended solids to settle out behind the dam, so that less food is available in the water downstream. This can subtly change the whole ecology of the downstream valley.

Only when costs like these are ignored can hydro power be considered cheap. Canada is one of the very few areas of the world with any remaining potential for significant hydro development. The strenuous resistance to these two projects—James Bay and the Churchill River diversion—is a clue to the future of such development in this country. It would seem that most of the few remaining sites can be developed only at very high cost, in terms of both intangibles and dollars.

The whole question of the costs, benefits and future possibilities of nuclear energy is another area of intense controversy. But there is no doubt that nuclear fission energy is here to stay, and over the next few decades it will supply a bigger and bigger share of our energy demands. Not even its most ardent proponents, however, would suggest that enough nuclear energy can or will be available to fill the gap left by dwindling fossil fuel reserves at any time in the foreseeable future. Even given its relatively minor role in supplying demand over the coming decades, nuclear energy will present a staggering problem in terms of the necessity for virtually perpetual storage of immense quantities of radioactive wastes. At just one of the three major radioactive waste storage centres in the United States, at Hanford, Washington, more than 74 million gallons of radioactive liquids are already being held in underground steel tanks, each equipped with its own cooling system. To date, about 200,000 gallons of this highly lethal brew has escaped into the ground through accidents. This tank storage system is seen as only a temporary stop-gap until a more permanent solution is found. The search goes on. If nuclear power in the United States grows as projected, by the year 2000, six billion curies of strontium 90 alone will be under perpetual storage. That is roughly as much strontium 90 as would be released during an all-out nuclear war. It takes considerably less than one curie of strontium 90 to kill a human.

Perhaps the best hope for the future, the distant future, lies in the development of the fusion reactor (as opposed to the *fission* reactors mentioned above). This involves the harnessing of the vast power released by the explosion of a hydrogen bomb. If the trick can be done (and as yet no one has been able to demonstrate that it can be) we will have a reactor that produces virtually no dangerous wastes and uses hydrogen isotopes available from sea water as a fuel.

The large-scale use of direct solar energy seems a slightly less remote prospect. There is reason to hope that before too long it may be feasible to begin to harness the sun on a community or even individual-dwelling level to supplement traditional power sources. In some parts of the world, solar energy is already being harnessed to do such jobs as providing hot water. Solar cells, used in conjunction with batteries or other energy storage devices, and perhaps supplemented with small amounts of conventionally produced electricity, could conceivably provide a significant fraction of domestic electricity needs. The prospect becomes brighter as the price of the cells (which convert sunlight to electricity) continues to fall and the prices of the alternative conventional energy sources go on spiralling upward.

There are several other less important potential power sources which we can also expect to see exploited on a local or regional basis. Three of the more promising are geothermal or underground steam power, tidal power and wind power. None of these seems capable of serving any significant fraction of our energy requirements as currently forecast. Reserves of underground steam are relatively small and widely dispersed, suitable tidal races are scarce (although Nova Scotia has the best) and wind is fickle. The production of methane gas and liquid methanol from sewage and other organic matter (discussed at length in chapter five) seems to hold considerable promise; but, again, neither fuel can be expected to be available in quantities large enough to fill any more than a small percentage of projected energy demands.

Before leaving this question of costs and potential benefits of various sources of energy, brief note should be taken of some of the energy-associated environmental problems that are truly global in scale. These are the problems which, more than any others, tend to make insomnia victims out of environmental scientists, and which could impose the ultimate limits on growth in energy use.

The first is oil in the oceans. About two million tons of oil are dumped into the world's oceans each year by ships, drilling rigs, industrial facilities and so on. A further estimated two million tons finds its way into the oceans from the oil-polluted atmosphere. A major portion of the earth's oxygen supply comes from ocean plant life; there is some evidence that oil is threatening that oxygen-producing capability. More specifically, Commander Jacques Yves Cousteau, the French oceanographer, has estimated that biological activity of all kinds in the oceans has been reduced by 30 to 50 per cent over the past twenty years by oil and other pollutants.

The second problem is waste heat. While there is considerable scientific disagreement as to just when it might happen, there is no argument over the fact that waste heat from power plants and other sources will eventually begin to modify the earth's climate if energy use continues to increase. One effect could be melting of the polar ice caps and subsequent flooding of coastal areas. Regional climatic alterations could well become important problems by the end of the century.

To sum up, we are fast running out of our main (and *only* portable) sources of energy and none of the alternative sources seems capable in the short or even medium run of supplying anything like the forecast requirements for energy in a world where demand for electricity alone doubles every eight and a half years. We obviously must cut back on demand. And the most urgent reason is not because reserves are running short, but because the environment will not be able to withstand the impact of the continued increases in pollution in forms such as thermal effects, gas emissions, transmission line rights-of-way, the destruction of scarce agricultural land through strip mining, and the whole Pandora's box of secondary pollution effects resulting from continued expansion of energy-dependent industry.

The energy shortage is unhappily only the first of a whole series of shocks, in the form of diminishing supplies of non-renewable resources, that are lurking just over the horizon. The Club of Rome's seminal study, *The Limits to Growth*, lists a number of resources which it forecasts will have been mostly used up within the next thirty-odd years if current rates of growth in consumption are permitted to continue. The predictions are based on figures for world reserves which have been prepared by the U.S. Bureau of Mines. Working on the assumption that new reserves may well be discovered as looming scarcity encourages exploration, the study also lists revised predictions which assumed a fivefold increase in known reserves. Here are the projections:

Resource	At Current Rates of Growth Reserves Would Last . . .	5 × Known Reserves Would Last . . .
Aluminum	31	55
Copper	21	48
Gold	9	29
Lead	21	64
Mercury	13	41
Molybdenum	34	65
Natural Gas	22	49
Petroleum	20	50
Silver	13	42
Tin	15	61
Tungsten	28	72
Zinc	18	50

(The figures do not take into account undersea reserves. In the case of copper, to choose one example, these could add 25 per cent to total land reserves, but only at great expense in terms of money and energy.)

Of course, the depletion of resource reserves involves a much more complex set of factors than simply known reserves and rates of growth in consumption. When a resource becomes scarce, four things happen: price increases reduce demand; exploration increases reserves (assuming all reserves have not already been discovered); scrap is recycled more carefully; and substitution for the scarce resource with more plentiful and cheaper alternatives is made wherever possible.

All of these measures tend to lengthen the life of reserves. But the reprieve is not as long as might be expected, unless the rate of growth in consumption is substantially reduced by price increases and substitution effects. Take chromium as an example. Simple rate-of-growth calculations show chromium reserves effectively exhausted (that is, usage falls to near zero) in 95 years if current rates of growth in use (2.5 per cent a year) continue. With five times known reserves, the predicted life is stretched to 154 years. However, complex computer projections done by the Club of Rome, taking into account all the factors mentioned above, show chromium reserves effectively exhausted in 125 years—roughly halfway between the two figures based on the simple rate-of-growth calculations. If reserves are doubled in the computer program, the figure rises to only 145 years. In any case, major economic dislocations caused by soaring prices could be expected to be experienced long before use of the resource fell to near zero.

There are a number of reasons why price increases and the substitution effect can be expected to have relatively little success in extending the predicted life of the resources listed above. To mention only two of the most important: all of these resources are vital to modern industry and therefore will continue to be used despite price increases simply because they are so necessary; and substitution is limited because in many cases sources of substitute materials are also running short. Aluminum has been used to substitute for increasingly expensive copper in power-line construction, but now aluminum, too, is becoming more expensive as economically accessible reserves dwindle. Plastics, seen as substitutes for many metals, are in seriously short supply because reserves of the petroleum from which they are synthesized are getting scarce. And so it goes. Synthesizing of substitutes, it should also be noted, normally requires far more energy than the usual mining and refining procedures. Nor should it be forgotten that energy consumption in mining and refining increases as poorer ore bodies come into production.

It seems clear that serious economic dislocation resulting from soaring prices for a number of vital non-renewable resources can be expected before the end of this century. The only choices open to us are whether to plan ahead to try to minimize the effects or to let market forces have their head, and let the chips fall where they may.

In view of the coming scarcities of these other non-renewable resources, it is instructive to take a look at our reaction to the shortage of gas and oil that began to be felt early in 1973. It can also be depressing. The search for some small indication that, somewhere, there is a responsible leader in North America who recognizes that the current energy crisis is merely a mild symptom of a profound sickness is all but fruitless.

Prime Minister Trudeau's long energy pep-talk in November 1973 contained just one paragraph that would indicate some sort of long-term perspective: "There may be inconveniences in the months ahead," he said, adding, "But I think each of us will better understand that squandering energy is not a privilege of our way of life, but a threat to it." The tone of the speech as a whole is better exemplified by a paragraph like this one:

> This combination of less security, higher prices and greater demand has led to exciting new development possibilities for relatively costly and remote energy sources, such as those in the huge Alberta oil sands, the Arctic and the Atlantic continental shelf.

There are those who would characterize such possibilities as desperate stopgaps rather than "exciting new developments."

In the United States, President Nixon assured his fellow Americans:

> As we look to the future, we can do so confident that the energy crisis will be resolved, not only for our time, but for all time. We will once again have those plentiful supplies of inexpensive energy which helped to build the greatest industrial nation and one of the highest standards of living in the world. The capacity for self-sufficiency in energy is a great goal, and an essential goal. We are going to achieve it.

Not a word did he say about the need for long-term cutbacks in demand. There was no hint of where he expects to find the resources to meet the approximately 100 per cent increase over today's needs that is projected for 1980.

In Alberta's Crowsnest Pass—coal-mining country—the editor of the local newspaper rejoiced: "They said 20 years ago we'd be the Pittsburgh of Canada. Now, there's no doubt about it, we're going to be." And in case any doubt remained as to what he had in mind, he added with apparent relish: "The forest reserves have to go, the mountains are going to have to go. There's no substitute for industrial development. The government [of Alberta] knows that. There are 400,000 people in Calgary who need the produce we have."

In Ontario, provincial energy minister Darcy McKeough advised motorists to disconnect anti-smog devices (a trick which, besides being illegal, would probably *increase* gasoline consumption without a complete retuning of the engine and re-jetting of the carburetor), and wistfully told the legislature: "It would be my hope, being somewhat on the sentimental side, that people would still be able to put up Christmas tree lights—perhaps not leave them on quite as long as they normally would or not leave them on all night." Members of the legislature, he said, "should be very delighted that Ontario Hydro and this government are able to say today that we do not have an electric power shortage." As for tomorrow, Mr. McKeough's misty-eyed vision apparently does not extend that far.

And, naturally, advice for homeowners on how they can cut fuel consumption proliferated; one could probably have got through the winter just by burning the lists in a wood stove—if wood stoves hadn't been in such short supply. Tips ranged all the way from the obvious things like insulating the attic and cleaning furnace air filters to an obscure suggestion from one province's energy department to "buy a pressure cooker." The majority of the suggestions are about as likely to solve the energy crisis (or even to significantly alleviate it) as picking up gum wrappers is to solve the pollution problem. The campaigns serve mainly to divert public attention from the real issues, away from the fact that truly constructive action can come only from government and industry. They give people a purely illusory feeling that as individuals they are somehow able to control events, and in doing so such campaigns do far more harm than good. They waste precious time.

On the international scene there was the saddening spectacle of the Japanese government succumbing to Arab demands and announcing a new pro-Arab Mid-East policy. Debate in Ottawa on the Mid-East situation was effectively if subtly muzzled, with External Affairs Minister Mitchell Sharp behaving like a man walking on eggs, justifiably fearful of offending the Arab leaders. Sabre-rattling in the United States was met by an Arab promise to destroy their own oil wells should the U.S. intervene militarily—a measure that would mean economic disaster on an unprecedented scale for the industrialized world. American politicians countered this by threatening to cut off food supplies to the Arab nations, a barbaric idea at best. Angered at not being able to suck Canada's oil reserves dry at rock-bottom prices, other Americans responded to Ottawa's minimal export restrictions by calling Canadians "blue-eyed Arabs." Common Market negotiations on unrelated subjects were disrupted by the venomous atmosphere of guilt and accusation stemming from the different treatment the Arabs accorded to different Common Market nations.

Whether the Arab states are justified in using their immense petroleum reserves as a political lever is not at issue here. But in that connection the Americans (and to a lesser extent Canadians, too) could perhaps be reminded of their own recent economic sanctions against Castro's Cuba and Allende's Chile, to give just two examples. In any event, it can be argued that, in their own perverse way, the Arab nations have done us a favour. By artificially creating a mini-energy crisis they have given us a jarring glimpse into the not-too-distant future when, unless we begin to plan now, conditions will be immeasurably worse. The embargo has forced a badly needed reassessment of our energy policies, perhaps in time for us to be in a position to minimize some of the effects of the real crisis to come.

Could one dare to hope that, in the light of this recent dismal experience, some thought might now be given to the looming shortages of other non-renewable resources? It is only necessary to note the location of the major foreign sources of minerals imported by the United States to become aware of the potential for diplomatic mischief. These, along with the percentage of total consumption imported, are listed in Table 1.

TABLE 1   PERCENTAGE OF U.S. MINERAL REQUIREMENTS
            IMPORTED DURING 1972

Mineral	Percentage imported	Major foreign sources
Platinum group metals	100	U.K., U.S.S.R., South Africa, Canada, Japan, Norway
Mica (sheet)	100	India, Brazil, Malagasy
Chromium	100	U.S.S.R., South Africa, Turkey
Strontium	100	Mexico, Spain
Cobalt	98	Zaire, Belgium, Luxembourg, Finland, Canada, Norway
Tantalum	97	Nigeria, Canada, Zaire
Aluminum* (ores and metal)	96	Jamaica, Surinam, Canada, Australia
Manganese	95	Brazil, Gabon, South Africa, Zaire
Fluorine	87	Mexico, Spain, Italy, South Africa
Titanium (rutile)	86	Australia
Asbestos	85	Canada, South Africa
Tin*	77	Malaysia, Thailand, Bolivia
Bismuth	75	Mexico, Japan, Peru, U.K., Korea
Nickel	74	Canada, Norway
Columbium	67	Brazil, Nigeria, Malagasy, Thailand
Antimony	65	South Africa, Mexico, U.K., Bolivia
Gold*	61	Canada, Switzerland, U.S.S.R.
Potassium	60	Canada
Mercury*	58	Canada, Mexico
Zinc*	52	Canada, Mexico, Peru
Silver*	44	Canada, Peru, Mexico, Honduras, Australia
Barium	43	Peru, Ireland, Mexico, Greece
Gypsum	39	Canada, Mexico, Jamaica
Selenium	37	Canada, Japan, Mexico, U.K.
Tellurium	36	Peru, Canada
Vanadium	32	South Africa, Chile, U.S.S.R.
Petroleum (includes liquid natural gas)*	29	Central and South America, Canada, Middle East
Iron	28	Canada, Venezuela, Japan, Common Market (EEC)
Lead*	26	Canada, Australia, Peru, Mexico
Cadmium	25	Mexico, Australia, Belgium, Canada, Luxembourg, Peru
Copper*	18	Canada, Peru, Chile
Titanium (ilmenite)	18	Canada, Australia

Rare earths	14	Australia, Malaysia, India
Pumice	12	Greece, Italy
Salt	7	Canada, Mexico, Bahamas
Cement	5	Canada, Bahamas, Norway
Magnesium (nonmetallic)	8	Greece, Ireland
Natural gas*	9	Canada
Rhenium	4	West Germany, France
Stone	2	Canada, Mexico, Italy, Portugal

SOURCE: Data derived from *Mining and Minerals Policy 1973*, a report by the Secretary of the Interior to the U.S. Congress.

Note: Minerals noted earlier in chapter as being in short supply are marked with asterisk. Compatible information for molybdenum and tungsten, both in short supply, is not available. Seventy-three per cent of world tungsten reserves are in China. The U.S. has 58 per cent of molybdenum reserves; the U.S.S.R. has 28 per cent. U.S. imports of non-fuel minerals cost $6 billion in 1971. It is forecast that this will rise to $20 billion by 1985 and to $50 billion by 2000.

Embargos are not the only tactics to fear from politically ambitious states possessing relatively large reserves of scarce materials. As the oil shortage has demonstrated, the high prices that result from scarcity and cartel price-fixing can mean immense wealth for the states in which remaining reserves are found. The huge gold and convertible currency reserves (mostly sterling and dollars) of the Arab states hang like a Sword of Damocles over the international monetary system. On December 6, 1973, the London stock exchange recorded the biggest drop in prices in its history when it was rumoured that some Arab leaders were about to get out of sterling with part of their $9 billion holdings in American and British banks. (These holdings could rise to $60 billion by 1980.) Were the Arabs to exchange their sterling for other currencies, it would mean disaster for the British economy as well as the international monetary system, commentators explained. The power that can accrue to small nations rich in scarce resources is hardly less than that to be gained by possession of nuclear weapons.

The growing power and influence of other members of the less-developed third world should also be a matter of concern for the rich nations in these days of diminishing supplies. China must have quite a different perspective on the matter of dwindling world energy resources by virtue of the fact that her total yearly energy consumption for a population of seven hundred million is less than is used annually in the United States for air conditioning. It would be more than a little surprising not to find resentment of American profligacy in China and other third world nations. The same picture could be painted in the cases of other resources as well: North Americans, 6 per cent of the world's population, consume a third of the world's yearly production of resources of all kinds.

Third world nations have still other reasons for bitterness when they consider their history, particularly the former colonial "dependencies." Not only did the present industrialized nations enjoy the immense benefits of getting all the most accessible reserves simply because they were first in, but they got them at bargain basement prices. Nearly all the manganese was stripped from Ghana at no more cost than subsistence wages for native labourers. Millions of tons of oil left the Middle East for Europe and North America under similar conditions until Arab nationalists began demanding a better deal twenty years ago. It will be difficult, during the coming decades, for the industrialized nations to deny the justice of third world demands for a bigger share of the world's resources. Such a redistribution would obviously add further to the supply problems of the rich nations. And the political adjustments that will have to be made almost defy imagination.

The whole philosophy in the rich nations concerning aid to the developing nations has been based on the "trickle down" theory: the idea is that the richer the rich nations get, the more of that wealth will find its way down to the poor nations in terms of increased production of primary materials to feed the industries of the rich, in increased employment in exotic fruit plantations, in increased tourism, and so on. It is a transparently self-serving philosophy that has provided the justification for minuscule foreign aid programs and has rankled the nations of the third world for decades. In any case, its credible life seems limited, since it assumes that growth and material enrichment can carry on indefinitely. The falseness of this premise will become abundantly clear as the industrialized economies begin to run up against vanishing resource reserves. When the trickle-down theory meets its doom in this way, the only way left to raise the standards of living in the poor nations will be some kind of direct international redistribution of wealth.

The same conclusions can be applied as well to the individual states within the international community; governments that have for centuries placated their poor by raising the total national income without, however, closing the gap between rich and poor will be forced, finally, to confront the question of income disparities. Growth will no longer serve as a substitute for genuine equity. In a state, as in a world, that has bumped up against limits to growth imposed by resource shortages and the need for conservation, there must be a ceiling on affluence. And, presumably, there will be a wish to establish a floor below which no one is allowed to fall. It follows that, the higher the floor below which no one is allowed to fall, the lower must be the ceiling above which no one is allowed to rise. To state this is not to preach socialism. It is simply to state conclusions made unavoidable by two facts: national or international systems which perpetuate economic injustice cannot be expected to last much longer in the global village; and rapidly approaching limits to resource exploitation, both physical and financial, are beginning to impose restraints on continued economic growth.

It would seem clear that government policy which aims to reduce social and economic dislocation arising out of resource scarcities must take account of these facts and bend with them rather than resist them. This means deliberately designing policies of "no-growth," in the economic sense. Or, to use a more positive phrase, it means planning a "steady-state" economy. Such an economic system would take account of the finite nature of resource reserves by changing from an emphasis in the economy on "throughput" to promotion of conservation of resources. The way a nation's well-being is currently measured in the Western world, we are seen as being better off if we consume two barrels of oil rather than one, if our aluminum factories can dispose of three million tons of ore instead of just two million. Inflationary price increases that may result from the increased pressure on scarce resources that this policy implies are seen as an external problem that must be dealt with separately.

In the steady-state economy quite the opposite reasoning is

used. One starts from the realization that reserves of non-renewable resources in the world are limited. Whether that limit is imposed by unrealistic costs involved in the exploitation of reserves containing only relatively minute quantities of the desired materials, or of reserves located in relatively inaccessible locations, or of reserves whose exploitation involves unrealistic environmental costs as when scarce agricultural land must be sacrificed forever to strip mining; or whether that limit is simply the physical one of exhaustion of all known reserves, makes no difference. Working with that assumption, the unavoidable judgment is made that the less of any given non-renewable resource we can get away with using without causing a decline in the quality of life, the better off we are.

There is an important distinction to be made here between "standard of living," a phrase that grows out of the growth-oriented economy, and "quality of life," a phrase more relevant in the steady-state system. Strictly defined, standard of living is a function of consumer goods and services per capita; a measure of material prosperity. In calculating standards of living, economists feel entitled to assume that goods exist to satisfy wants that would be present even if the goods were not. Any increase in the standard of living is thus held to be a good thing. But it is by no means clear that goods which, for instance, carry their own wants with them through clever advertising (like vaginal deodorants) are a good thing. Surely the value of goods really lies in their utility rather than their abundance or price. And surely a distinction must be made between "wants" and "needs."

Quality of life implies an evaluation of needs more than wants—first, physical needs like food and shelter, and then a host of spiritual or psychic needs which are ignored in the concept of standard of living, the most fundamental of which is opportunity. Fulfil the basic physical needs of a group, provide them with the opportunity to satisfy as many of the range of psychic needs as they care to, and they will have the potential for a high quality of life. Goods and services can certainly be important to the attainment of a high quality of life in the sense, first, that they can provide for basic physical needs and, secondly, that they can provide the raw material for self-fulfilment. To the extent that they provide neither, they do nothing to raise the quality of life on this planet and may, in fact, even lower it—through pollution, for example.

How would the move toward a steady-state economy affect the auto industry, for example? Much of the strength of the North American economy is based on the ever-increasing output of this industry, which purchases immense and ever-growing amounts of resources of many kinds and puts them through a manufacturing process whose end product is cars and trucks. Because of the way in which we do our economic accounting, the more resources put through this system, the higher the gross national product climbs and the better off we are seen to be. So, in order to increase this throughput, the industry has devised a number of schemes, the most notorious of which is planned obsolescence. Not only are cars deliberately designed to fall apart far more quickly than need be the case, but yearly model changes and the subtle pressure of carefully researched advertising encourages the consumer to think of the car as a disposable or throw-away product. Design criteria also ensure that maximum damage is done to the vehicle in any given accident, so that more resources can be put through the system to provide replacement parts. Moreover, there is little pressure to make cars which use fuel efficiently, since increased efficiency here means less throughput in the closely related oil industry and is thus "bad for the economy."

It hardly needs to be pointed out that this scheme of things has led to an immense squandering of resources over the years, a profligacy for which we are now only beginning to pay the price. And it is also worth mentioning, parenthetically, that if pollution can be thought of as the needless waste of energy or material that is dumped into the environment rather than being collected and re-used, it becomes clear that this throughput system has built into it a strong incentive to pollute. This incentive must be counteracted later at high cost through anti-pollution technology and waste disposal programs.

In the steady-state economy, the waste generated by the auto industry would become a negative input to the national accounts; the measure of national well-being, or whatever phrase might be chosen to replace GNP, would *increase* to whatever extent waste could be reduced. The drive would be to produce the most efficient, crash-resistant, compact, durable vehicle possible with known technology—in other words, to keep throughput as low as possible. The initial cost of such a vehicle might be higher than is normally paid nowadays (but not necessarily, given our talent for innovative engineering); however, it seems likely that the consumer would wind up paying less in the long run. This is certainly the case if reduced costs to the taxpayer for environmental damage and time lost through accidents are taken into account.

Without wading too deeply into the murky waters of pricing, two further points can be made. First, it has been well demonstrated in policy-planning institutions in Canada, the United States and Europe that the computer-assisted systems dynamics techniques needed to bring about a relatively smooth conversion to a steady-state economy (a conversion that would take full account of pricing problems) exist and are workable. Secondly, it can be expected that as the conversion is being made over a period of years, even decades, people's attitudes will continue to change from a primary concern with standard of living (i.e. with conspicuous consumption and accumulation of artifacts) to a new concern for the quality of life. This trend, which may already be in evidence, should have a profound effect of its own on prices. To borrow an aphorism from Oscar Wilde, there may in future be fewer of those who know the price of everything and the value of nothing. One could hope that, having experienced the sharply diminishing returns associated with accumulation beyond certain limits of material wealth, people will be content with less in the way of physical goods and demand instead more opportunity to furnish the mind and spirit.

No one in a position to assess the facts can any longer doubt that the steady-state economy is coming. Either it will be imposed through a series of disastrously disruptive, scarcity-bred depressions (the first of which we may be about to experience), or else it can come through staged social and economic planning.*

* See Appendix 1.

2.
The Northern Frontier

The Arctic—that part of the country lying north of the 60th parallel where the provinces end and the Yukon and Northwest Territories begin—covers 40 per cent of the Canadian land mass, and is home for about sixty-five thousand people. Slightly more than half of these people are natives: Métis, Indians and Eskimos or Inuit. The Indians and Inuit inhabited the Arctic long before the white man knew North America existed, and in that sense, the Arctic is their land. For the vast majority of these natives, the land and its resources form part of the personal identity, part of their culture. The land is therefore not something to be bought and sold any more than one buys or sells his sense of humour. The city-dwelling Canadian to the south, by now completely alienated from the land, finds this attitude incomprehensible. And because it is the southern non-native who holds the power, it is inevitable that the north will be opened up and that its petroleum reserves will be exploited to feed an increasingly energy-hungry industrial empire in southern Canada and the United States. In opening up the north, we will be following the doctrine that has governed exploitation of North America since the first European settlements began to appear on the continent's eastern shores: those who can make the most economically productive use of the land have an overriding right to it. Armed with this scientifically rational, though morally dubious, ideology, we seldom feel the need to listen closely to what is being said by the tiny minorities to whom this philosophy is alien. To help keep some balance in the following collage of facts and ideas on development of the petroleum potential of Canada's north, it seems appropriate to give the opening words to a senior Inuit hunter from Grise Fiord on the south coast of Ellesmere Island, northernmost island in the Arctic archipelago.

The comments were taped in 1972 at the request of Roderick

Riewe, a participant from the University of Manitoba in an International Biological Programme project in the region. The people of the hamlet were asked to describe their hunting grounds and hunting techniques. They took the opportunity to also express their concern at the invasion of their land by oil exploration teams, and asked Riewe to make the tapes available to the white man. Here (in translation) is an extract from one of the tapes:

Caribou have always been very scarce and it is the hardest animal to hunt during summer because you can't go very far or in just any direction during summer. The only times the people here can hunt caribou are in September and October, and then only by going inland. It is very hard for people here to get inland and it is a lot of work, mainly because of bare rock. There is no other route. There are caribou inland, up near Eureka, but today there are none near the coast. And that area is always visited by white people and without our knowledge. We see lots of oil barrels near that area where we do our caribou hunting, and every time we go there during the caribou hunting season there are more oil barrels.

But we do know they have been there; they leave many things, like oil drums, that are not very tasteful to caribou. It is as bad as people being there. We have not given our consent for people to go there. We have not given any permission to anyone to do any kind of building or settling there. No one has told us anything about that area, or who is moving there or who is building there. We have no idea who is going there. No one told us anything and yet it is the only area where we go caribou hunting. And caribou are one of our food resources. It is causing very much unhappiness among people here to find gas and oil drums in that area.

It is good that people are interested in animal life but very often there are unnecessary airplanes carrying photographers, flying around over the heads of caribou and muskox. We feel that our animal resources are being chased away by airplane noise. Recently, I decided to hunt caribou in the area that used to be full of caribou. I didn't see one caribou there. There were more oil barrels than caribou there. They were empty but a great nuisance as litter. We know the caribou now run to places they have never been before. . . .

We have no plans whatever to stop caribou hunting, not only for the meat, but for the fur which is the only kind of clothing we could be active in during the winter. Money could never replace caribou skins; even if we had a lot of money there are no other ways we could dress for the weather here. We couldn't move, even to the nearest place, without caribou skins. Imagine if the caribou were further away than they are now! The caribou have many uses: not just their skins and meat, but also their sinew. It is the sinew that we use to sew our boots that are made of sealskin. There is nothing that can replace caribou sinew because the sinew is used to make waterproof clothing. It is impossible to live here without caribou. Caribou are needed without end by the Inuit. . . .

Craig Harbour has always been a seal hunting area in winter: it still is and the seals are still plentiful there. There are still just enough to feed the people. As you know, in the past we used to have a lot of seals in order to feed the dogs as well as people, but now we get just enough to feed people. It seems much harder to get seals now than it used to be. We need seals, not just for food, but for skins to trade to the Co-op, in order to get cash. Seal meat has always been the year-round food for the people. It can be taken any time. It is very nice to have a change of food, like caribou, when they are in season, but still, the seal can never be replaced by these foods, even though caribou meat is a real delicacy and very nice to have. We have no plans at all to stop hunting as long as they're around. Not, at least, until the white man has wiped them out or other destructive things happen. The survival of Inuit people will be in danger if the seals begin to disappear. There are many things that can disturb these animals, like oil activity: oil searchers come around and the food of the seal is destroyed, then there is no real food for the people and so the survival of the people here is endangered. I think the seal has many uses, not only for men and not only for dogs but also for animals like polar bears, so if the seal were to disappear completely there is no hope.

I am very concerned about oil drillers, oil seekers, because I understand very well that one day the South, the white man's land, will run out of oil and they will gradually come this way, North, to look for oil. And it is this I am not ready for. People are not willing to see these things, now we know they are very destructive to animal life. I am not ready to accept the disappearance of animals. I know I am not the boss, nor am I speaking the last word for anyone, but I understand that animals will not last when machines or more people come here to the north. . . .

I am not concerned just for me, nor am I trying to build any kind of unpleasant feeling toward anyone, but the animals will not survive here with oil drillers. We cannot build animals; we cannot make animals; they have to be here by nature. . . . The government makes a lot of money from the people who are connected with oil exploration, but we, the people here, do not receive any money. It would seem more sensible if we, the people, were to receive a lot of money and we are the ones who should be the first to hear. People just come in and build, even before they speak to us. This is indeed very uncomfortable, and then the government says, "be responsible."

There are just too many white people who think the Inuit have no sense at all. Some of them believe we have no ability to think just because we are without their method of learning. It is very easy to notice a well-educated white man—he is usually very helpful. But there are others who might as well forget you are there.

The habits of the caribou and the other animals I have spoken about have been known to us from generation to generation. It is from our ancestors that we learned these facts. And food here does not have one home, it moves around and has to be searched for. Food does not will itself to be here. It should be known that food is hard to get here. There is no easy access to our hunting areas; in order for us to do our hunting we must expand these areas. There are not many directions we could travel from Grise Fiord, but if we have to go further beyond our hunting areas, we will do so. No one is ever going to stop us hunting here in our land.

From its beginnings in 1947 up to the end of 1970, oil and gas exploration in Canada's Arctic saw a total expenditure of $415 million. By the end of 1974 this total will have more than doubled, to an estimated $948 million, as the oil industry scrambles to find the huge reserves necessary to fill the widening gap in North America between demand and supply of petroleum. The country being probed by seismic recorders and tapped by test wells is, next to Antarctica itself, the bleakest, most forbidding in the world. Over much of its extent the average temperature in winter (when most of the drilling work must be done) is about 20 degrees Fahrenheit below zero, and high winds often make that feel more like 80 or 90 below. To combat the problems posed by weather and isolation, the oil industry is using technology that is almost unimaginably sophisticated. Communications for at least one company are provided by a portable earth station which links frontier exploration and drilling crews with head offices in southern Alberta through the ANIK 1 communications satellite. Crews are transported in balloon-tired vehicles similar to those proposed for freight transport on the moon. Supplies are ferried

TABLE 2   ULTIMATE RECOVERABLE POTENTIAL OF CANADIAN ARCTIC

	Oil (billion bbl.)	Gas (trillion cu. ft.)
Arctic Islands (land and offshore)	20.3	242.0
Mackenzie Delta	6.2	93.5
Mainland NWT	1.7	7.5
Baffin Island (slope and shelf)	14.7	91.3
Total	42.9	434.3

SOURCE: Based on 1973 Geological Survey of Canada evaluation. Figures are highly speculative.

from place to place by short take-off and landing (STOL) aircraft, helicopters and hovercraft. To protect the tundra from erosion that would follow destruction of the thin insulating layer of soil and vegetation, conventional wheeled and tracked vehicles follow roads of packed snow: when snow was late in appearing in the autumn of 1973, one company (in its impatience) imported a snow-making machine built for southern ski slopes. In the Beaufort Sea north of the Mackenzie River delta, artificial islands are being built in the shallow waters to support drilling rigs. Ice, in chunks measuring five feet square and ten feet deep, weighing seven tons, is cut and lifted away by cranes; gravel trucked sixty-five miles or more over frozen rivers is dumped into the hole until the surface of the "island" rises above the ice level. Chances of these islands surviving even one summer of ice-scouring during the break-up and violent storms in the brief open-water period (just a hundred days most years) are remote, so drilling equipment must be removed once temperatures start to rise, whether the test hole is completed or not.

The stakes in this Arctic exploration rush are obviously huge for the oil companies, which stand to make immense profits should substantial amounts of oil and gas be found, and should feasible transportation systems to the south be devised. Even greater stakes are involved for the Canadian people. The rapid opening up of the north to exploitation of gas and oil reserves means, among other things, a renewed long-term commitment to traditional policies of growth and consumerism which some Canadians have begun to reconsider in the light of recent information on the precarious state of health of the environment and on the remaining lifetime of reserves of many non-renewable resources. And because the Canadian market for oil and gas is not at present large enough to make Arctic transportation systems economically feasible, immediate exploitation of northern reserves would also mean new long-term commitments to export large quantities of oil and gas to the United States. Only by coupling these exports with Canadian demand can economies of scale large enough to bring transportation costs down to a reasonable level be realized immediately. It is being argued with increasing force that such exports would not be in the best interests of Canada, and that the cost to Canadians of playing a significant role in construction of transmission facilities on Canadian soil at this time would cause serious disruptions in the Canadian economy.

Beyond a government aerial survey of the region in 1947 and a few small, tentative exploration probes arising out of publication of the survey photographs, very little interest was shown in the resources of Canada's north before 1960. In that year the federal government (Ottawa has control of all resources in lands above the 60th parallel) got together with representatives of the oil industry to work out land regulations that would give the industry enough incentive to begin exploring in the unfriendly region. So favourable were these arrangements that twelve-year exploration permits covering 60 million acres or 93,600 square miles had been snapped up within weeks of promulgation of the new regulations. No rent was paid for the permits; instead, the companies were required to agree to spend, in the first year, 5 cents an acre on exploration. Enough money to cover this cost was placed on deposit with the government, to be returned at the end of the year when the company demonstrated it had done the amount of work required of it. After the third year, the required exploration expenditure per acre began rising steadily to a total of $2.65, so that a company holding two million acres had to spend $5,300,000 over twelve years. Companies finding oil and gas were granted twenty-one-year leases on half the land covered by their permits, which would allow them, in most cases, to remove about three-quarters of the petroleum lying under the entire leased area. The royalty to be paid to the government was set at 5 per cent for the first three to five years, depending on the location of the wells, and then rose to 10 per cent. Until 1970 (when the provision was revoked) the companies also had the right to lease the second half of their permit lands, provided they paid a higher royalty on gas and oil removed. Otherwise, this so-called corridor land reverted to the crown, for disposal by tender.

The provisions of the 1960 land regulations remain a source of consuming consternation for many Canadians, particularly the growing ranks of the nationalists. They point out that the foreign-owned corporations that asked for and received most of the permits will enjoy immense profits under the royalty provisions— which are among the world's most lenient. A portion of these profits, they argue, rightfully belongs to the Canadian public. In Alaska, where exploration and development conditions are similar, the royalty collected by the state amounts to 20 per cent, or twice the Canadian royalty, and the companies are also required to pay a heavy severance tax. Further revenues are gained by the state in Alaska because all leases are sold at auction, whereas in Canada's north they are granted to half the land covered by permit automatically and without additional cost to the exploration permit holder.

The government and the oil industry argue that the low royalties were necessary to encourage exploration of the north on a significant scale. Companies found it difficult to justify compliance with exploration requirements once the rate had risen to 15 cents an acre and, in fact, Gulf Oil Canada Limited and Shell Canada Limited decided at that point to drop some of their permits. Finds were few and far between compared to the exploration "play" in other parts of the world, and drilling costs were enormous—about three times those experienced to the south in Alberta or Texas.

With the discovery on Alaska's north slope by Atlantic Richfield of the huge Prudhoe Bay oil and gas reservoir in 1968, however, exploration in Canada's north exploded with new excitement. The amount of land under permit soared from 180 million acres to 320 million acres within twelve months of the find. By mid 1973 that had risen to 844 million acres, or about 1,320,000 square miles.

With the benefit of hindsight, and particularly in the light of the post-Prudhoe land rush, it is possible to argue that the Canadian government would have been well advised in 1960 to have been more conservative in its policy of encouraging northern exploration. It seems clear now that the Prudhoe Bay discovery, or even the Arab oil boycott of 1973-74, would have provided ample incentive for the oil industry to begin exploring Canada's north, even under more normal royalty arrangements. The price that will have to be paid for that early encouragement by the government will be enormous. Take gas royalties as an example. Assuming the Mackenzie Valley gas pipeline is built and that it carries half Prudhoe Bay gas and half Canadian Mackenzie delta gas to southern markets as currently proposed, at the expected wellhead price of 30 cents per thousand cubic feet, royalty payments to the Canadian government during the first three years of production would be about $36 million, while the government of Alaska would collect $144 million on the same amount of gas. In ensuing years Canadian royalties would amount to $24 million annually and Alaska's would be about $48 million. Total royalties from Mackenzie delta gas over ten years would be $204 million; for an equal amount of Prudhoe Bay gas, Alaska would collect $480 million. The same kind of disparity would, of course, apply to royalties on oil production as well.

The federal government has had these leasing arrangements under review since 1970. Although no official announcement had been made by early 1974, the authoritative industry magazine *Oilweek* reported that any revisions made would not apply to lands already held under lease or exploration permit. Thus, the existing royalty arrangements would continue to apply to well over 80 per cent of the total of 920 million acres of potential oil- and gas-bearing land in Canada's Arctic. It is speculated that a new royalty of 16.6 per cent would apply to the remaining lands.

Nonetheless, in the early 1960s exploration in the north was painfully slow despite government incentives. In the Mackenzie delta region, only Imperial Oil Limited saw fit to mount a large-scale operation. By 1964 the company held permits on 10 million acres in the delta. But it was not until January 1970 that it was able to announce its first discovery of gas at Atkinson Point. Since that time there have been two more major gas finds and two smaller oil discoveries by the company in the region. Shell, Gulf and Mobil have also now announced major gas discoveries.

In the Arctic islands, not even Imperial seemed ready in the early 1960s to make a major push. Beginning in 1964, attempts were made by Calgary geologist J. G. (Cam) Sproule to organize a cooperative exploration effort by a consortium of firms. But the big multinational oil companies weren't interested, and it was not until the federal government agreed in 1967 to put up 45 per cent of the money for the exploration program that Sproule's plan could be realized. The resulting consortium of nineteen private companies and the Canadian government was called Panarctic Oils Limited. By early 1974 it held permits for 60 million acres of land and had made five major gas discoveries and one oil find in the

Queen Elizabeth Islands north of the north magnetic pole. In all, twenty wells were drilled in the Arctic islands by Panarctic and the other major companies involved in island exploration in 1974 (Gulf, Imperial, Elf, Dome, Sunoco and others). To support drilling operations, 20,000 tons of equipment and materials and 20,000 tons of fuel were shipped into the Arctic archipelago in 1973 and again the following year. Five years earlier only two wells had been sunk.

Although the question of how gas discovered in the Mackenzie delta is to be transported south appears to have been settled (that is, by pipeline), it is still not certain how the oil thought to exist in large quantities in the adjacent Beaufort Sea, or the oil and gas in the Arctic islands to the north, is to be brought out to market.

Pipelines seem to have a headstart over other methods of Arctic gas and oil transportation as far as research and development go, but they are not without their own problems. The biggest headache arises out of the fact that the land in the Arctic is permanently frozen. Once an area begins to thaw through application of heat or because of destruction of the thin insulating layer of vegetation on the surface, a self-sustaining erosion process sets in that can continue indefinitely, expanding in all directions. The problem is particularly severe in soils with a high ice content. Tread marks left on ice-rich permafrost have been known to expand into twenty-foot mud sloughs which grow bigger each year through the combined effects of water erosion and radiant heat from the sun. Oil and gas come out of the ground at temperatures upwards of 150 degrees Fahrenheit; were this heat to be transferred to the permafrost by a pipeline, the result would be creation of a permanent, marshy canal perhaps fifty feet deep along the length of the pipe. This would not only present the threat of pipeline fracture, it could interfere with migration patterns of Arctic wildlife and thereby threaten the survival of affected species.

To overcome this problem, the consortium proposing to build the Mackenzie Valley gas pipeline plan to cool the gas to 30 degrees or lower, below the permafrost's melting point. To avoid damage to the insulating carpet of vegetation during construction, snow would be compacted into a road on which the heavy trenching and pipe-laying equipment could move. The fill taken from the trench would be scraped over the pipeline and mounded to a height of perhaps three feet, depending on how much settling during the summer months was predicted by soil analysis. Gravel could be added to ensure that the surface of the trench did not sink below the surrounding land and lead to water erosion along the line. It has also been suggested that Arctic grass be sown along the line to further inhibit erosion.

Oil, of course, would not flow freely if cooled to below the melting point of water, so an oil pipeline either buried in permafrost or resting on the surface would need to be completely insulated. Unfortunately, the techniques and materials for providing 100 per cent effective insulation for pipelines do not exist; some degree of erosion and the consequent risk of a pipeline fracture cannot, with present technology, be avoided. In the Soviet Union hot oil pipelines cross permafrost on high stilts; the permafrost is protected and there is no physical barrier to game migration (though there may be a psychological one). If this method were to be adopted for use on a line running south from the Mackenzie delta, at least 360 miles of pipeline would have to be elevated to protect high-ice permafrost areas.

The Mackenzie Valley Pipeline Research Limited, a sixteen-member industry consortium, has studied the feasibility of building an oil pipeline from Prudhoe Bay to Edmonton. The study was continued after the U.S. government decided to opt for the Trans-Alaska pipeline to the deep-water port of Valdez, where tankers would be loaded to carry the Prudhoe Bay oil south to west-coast American ports, because it is thought there may eventually be enough oil found in the Mackenzie delta–Beaufort Sea area to justify the pipeline even without Alaskan oil. Including the two-hundred-mile extension from Prudhoe Bay to the Mackenzie delta, the proposed 1.8 million-barrel-a-day line would cost an estimated $3.38 billion (in 1976 dollars). Operating costs were estimated at $80 million a year. Total transportation costs to Edmonton were put at about $1.15 a barrel; it would cost another 40 cents a barrel to move the oil from Edmonton to Chicago. Even at a low Chicago price of $4.00 a barrel for crude, it is clear that the line could be economically viable, provided that large oil deposits are discovered in the north and the present recovery cost of about 50 cents a barrel can be maintained. The probability of such finds was increased in March 1974 with Imperial Oil's announcement that a drill site on an artificial island in the Beaufort Sea had struck oil. Pipelines have also been suggested as a means of transporting oil and gas out of the Arctic islands. The engineering problems would be enormous, combining all the difficulties faced in mainland Arctic projects with the yet-unstudied problems of how to lay pipeline in deep Arctic waters and how to prevent ice-scouring in shallower water where ice floes move with irresistible, unimaginable force. Apparently confident that even these problems can be overcome with enough engineering skill and money, Panarctic Oil, in cooperation with TransCanada Pipelines Limited, Canadian Pacific Investments Limited and Tennaco Oil and Minerals Limited (Houston), has formed the Polar Gas Project to explore pipeline possibilities. Panarctic has already surveyed a route through the islands to the Boothia Peninsula; from there a line could run south down either the east or west coast of Hudson Bay to Toronto or Montreal (see map).

The other land-based transportation system under study is a rail line, which would run from the Mackenzie delta to the end of permafrost at Trout River, about one hundred miles east of Great Slave Lake and just north of the Alberta–Northwest Territories boundary at the 60th parallel. From there the oil would be carried to Edmonton by pipeline. Proponents of the railway see several advantages over pipelines: rail transport would all but eliminate the risk of damage to the permafrost and consequent erosion; it would provide for many more permanent jobs than a pipeline; and it would provide a rapid, all-weather, low-cost means of transportation for goods other than gas and oil in and out of the north. This latter point could have an important social impact on the north, where prices of food, building materials and other goods are already high and are expected to soar virtually out of sight once large-scale exploitation of northern petroleum begins.

A 1972 study by the Canadian Institute of Guided Ground Transport (at Queen's University) proposed a design based, for comparison with studies of Prudhoe Bay oil pipelines along the Mackenzie Valley, on Prudhoe Bay oil and gas supplies. The 1,100-mile rail line would be the most expensive ever constructed at $2.43 billion (somewhat less if the two-hundred-mile Mackenzie delta–Prudhoe Bay section were eliminated). Nonetheless, the

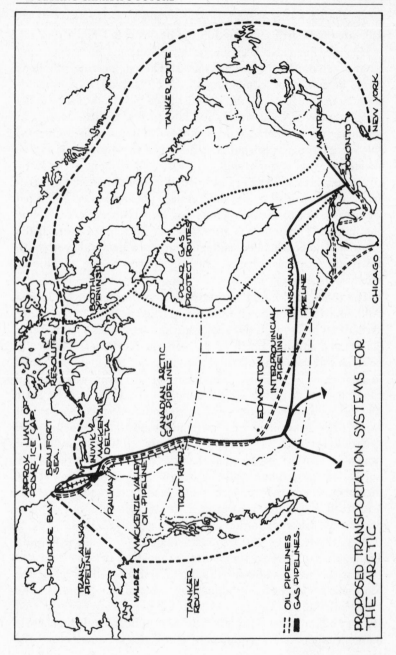

PROPOSED TRANSPORTATION SYSTEMS FOR THE ARCTIC

OIL PIPELINES
GAS PIPELINES.

combined cost of the rail line and the large-diameter pipeline from Trout Lake to the existing continental distribution system at Edmonton would be lower than the proposed all-pipe system. On the other hand, operating costs, estimated to be $58.3 million for wages and salaries to 4,600 permanent employees, $79.5 million for maintenance materials and $47.7 million for fuel—a total of $194 million a year—would be more than double the $80 million estimated for the highly automated pipeline. Higher interest rates paid on capital borrowed to build the more expensive pipeline system would reduce this difference to some extent. And the social benefits of the creation of so many permanent jobs in a high-unemployment area might outweigh any remaining disadvantage of these higher operating costs. (Such benefits are apparently poorly understood in some quarters of the oil industry: in what was meant to be a facetious editorial, *Oilweek's* editor suggested that as an alternative to the rail line the government should "set up a project to move oil and liquefied gas out of the Arctic with a force of 15 million Chinese coolies using wheelbarrows." The comment speaks eloquently of a stunning insensibility one can only hope is not widespread among northern developers.)

In addition to the 4,600 northern jobs, the study estimates that 13,000 new and permanent jobs would be created in manufacturing and supply industries in the south. The settlement at the Trout Lake terminus would blossom into a town of perhaps 25,000 inhabitants.

Some see a further advantage for the railway idea in that it would presumably be built and operated by Canadian National or Canadian Pacific Railways and would thus help weaken the chain of vertical integration within the oil industry that gives it such complete control over prices and marketing. It is also pointed out that all of the needed engineering and construction skills to build a railway exist in Canada, whereas the Arctic pipeline would rely to some extent on skilled labour imported from the United States.

The study envisioned a complete dual right-of-way over the entire length of the route, over which two billion barrels of oil would be carried daily in twenty trains, each of about 170 tank cars pulled by five diesel locomotives. The trains would travel at 60 miles per hour. By adding ten more trains a day plus gas liquefaction and re-gasification plants, the rail line could also carry enough natural gas to feed a large-diameter pipeline.

Total transportation costs per barrel of oil delivered to Chicago by the rail-pipeline system compare favourably to those of the all-pipe system, according to the study, at $1.07 a barrel. Gas could be moved to the same destination for about 60 cents per thousand cubic feet, which also seems to be well within competitive bounds.

The advantages of the rail line—protection of the permafrost, flexibility, job provision, cost and so on—must be balanced against the disadvantages. These include the impact of noise and the right-of-way itself on wildlife, and the need for very large quantities of gravel. A pipeline would unquestionably be quieter than a rail line although, with its huge pumping and compressor stations spaced every fifty miles along its length, it would be far from silent. And the fact that a railway would require between 400 and 500 million cubic yards of gravel as compared with about 42 million cubic yards for a pipeline needs to be balanced by pointing out that the railway can transport its own ballast from a few large pits, while ballast for the pipeline must be found all along the route north. The risk of oil spills, which are major calamities in the frozen north, would be substantially lower with the rail line, particularly at the numerous river crossings.

On balance, then, it can be argued that while the environmental impact of a rail line might be somewhat higher than that of a well-constructed oil pipeline, and very much higher than that of a buried gas pipeline, the social benefits it would bring to the people of the north in terms of job creation and lower transportation costs for non-petroleum goods could also be immeasurably greater.

Predictably, the oil industry strongly favours its own pipeline alternative, partly because it wants to protect its structure of vertical integration, but also because the pipeline could be built more quickly (in two and a half years as opposed to five years for the rail line), a consideration that carries considerably more weight in the United States than it need do in Canada, where conventional southern oil supplies provide self-sufficiency until 1980, with the tar sands available to fill the gap for some years after that, and where gas self-sufficiency from southern wells should extend to 1990 if reserves are used wisely and exports are curbed.

Unfortunately, the Canadian government has shown little

enthusiasm for the rail line, which is looked on almost exclusively as an oil-carrying system, preferring instead to allow the oil industry to make the decision as to which form of transportation should be used. By the winter of 1974, Canadian Arctic Gas Study Limited had spent upwards of $70 million on testing, research and preparation of its applications for construction of the Mackenzie Valley gas pipeline; Mackenzie Valley Pipeline Research, the other industry consortium, had spent more than $7 million on oil pipeline research. In contrast, government and the railway industry have spent just $2.5 million researching the rail alternative. Virtually none of this relatively meagre amount has been spent examining social costs and benefits, the area where the rail proposal holds most of its cards.

A third possibility for transporting oil and gas out of the Arctic —and one that will no doubt receive serious consideration where the Arctic island reserves are concerned—is the tanker ship. In normal conditions, the huge tankers of today, some over 500,000 deadweight tons, are even more economical than pipelines. And they have the added advantage of flexibility of destination. Their one major disadvantage is that they are prone to accident. The sinking of a large tanker anywhere in the world is a major disaster from the environmentalist's point of view; the sinking of a tanker in ice-choked Arctic waters would be a catastrophe of unimaginable proportions for the frail northern environment.

In 1969 Exxon and a group of partners from the oil industry refitted a 115,000-ton tanker, the *Manhattan*, for an experimental voyage through the Northwest Passage to Prudhoe Bay. The object was to examine the feasibility of a regular tanker route to the western Arctic oil basins. The ship, huge though it seemed alongside the Canadian ice breakers that assisted it, was a half-scale model of the vessel that would eventually be used in regular service. It made a successful round-trip run to Prudhoe Bay in September and then returned for another attempt in April 1970, when ice conditions were at their worst. Exxon pronounced the experiments a success, stating that ice-breaking tankers had been proved to be commercially practical. However, the Manhattan program was dropped, for the moment at least, because it was evident that, as far as Prudhoe Bay oil was concerned, a pipeline would be cheaper. Exxon went on to back the Trans-Alaska pipeline. But the threat of the tanker remains for the Arctic islands, where pipeline construction would be so enormously expensive as to make the ships competitive, even though they could be expected to cost between $75 million and $100 million each—twice as much as conventional tankers of comparable capacity.

Other engineers have approached the problem of Arctic ice with schemes to go under or over it in submarines and aircraft. General Dynamics Corporation has prepared a preliminary design for an oil-carrying nuclear submarine of 250,000 tons that would cruise at speeds of up to 17 knots, three to four hundred feet below the surface. It could either sail all the way to southern ports on the Atlantic seaboard, or it could transship its oil to conventional tankers at a port in Greenland. The company estimates the cost of such a sub-tanker at between $200 million and $255 million.

A Toronto-based organization called the Great Plains Group has proposed an air shipment scheme based on Boeing Corporation's design for a giant resource-carrying aircraft designated RC–1. The RC–1 would carry two giant removable pods under its wings, each the size of the fuselage of a Boeing 747 jumbo jet, with a total capacity of 46 million cubic feet of liquefied natural gas. The Great Plains Group projects a fleet of thirty-four RC–1s flying two return trips each to the Arctic islands every day, for a total carry-out of three billion cubic feet of gas a day. Sophisticated navigation techniques would ensure landing capability even in zero-visibility weather. Boeing estimates the cost of transport at 3 cents per thousand cubic feet per hundred miles. Liquefaction and regasification would cost another 30 or 40 cents per thousand cubic feet. So the cost of carrying gas from the high Arctic to the United States border would be in the neighbourhood of one dollar per thousand cubic feet.

Capital cost estimates for such a project are highly speculative, but Boeing says it could build a prototype RC–1 for about $1 billion, and that each subsequent plane would cost around $75 million (for a total initial investment of $3.5 billion). Another billion dollars or so would have to be invested in airports and liquefaction facilities.

The proposal is worth recording here mainly because it is an exemplary statement of the narrow engineering approach to problem-solving that has led North America to the position where it must consider taking the enormous risks involved in any form of resource exploitation in the high Arctic. The environmental hazards involved in operation of a fleet of oil- or gas-carrying RC–1 aircraft are manifestly huge (noise and air pollution problems pale beside the question: what if one should crash?); furthermore, the airplane is by far the most inefficient means of transport we have. Freight-carrying jets currently use sixty-five times as much energy per ton-mile as either ships or trains (or, presumably, submarines) and more than one hundred times as much as a pipeline. The Great Plains Group has spent $2 million so far researching the proposal; it is understandably having difficulty raising a further $10 million from the oil industry and the Canadian government to continue its studies.

To an outsider, talk of multi-billion-dollar transportation systems and a huge exploration program carried on in some of the world's most remote and hostile territory would indicate that Canada is facing an imminent shortage of gas and oil. What else could justify the risks and expenditures involved in these projects? The fact is, however, that Canada is one of the few industrial nations in the world with enough oil and gas in proved reserves to provide self-sufficiency beyond the end of this decade, and enough in potential (but so far unproved) reserves to last well beyond the end of this century. The federal Department of Energy, Mines and Resources in its recent study, *An Energy Policy for Canada*, estimates that "there is probably more than enough [oil and gas] to meet domestic requirements until at least the year 2050 with a possibility of substantial amounts of oil and gas being available for export. These forecasts are made on the basis of prices in the year 2000 which would not exceed ... $2 per thousand feet for natural gas and about $7 or $8 a barrel of oil [in 1972 dollars]." By 1974 gas prices were already approaching $1 a thousand cubic feet in some sales and Mid-East and Latin American oil prices had soared up to and beyond $10 a barrel. Proved reserves in the western provinces alone provide self-sufficiency in gas for the Canadian market until 1985 (assuming a price in the region of $1.25 per thousand cubic feet), and in oil (assuming limited tar sands production and a price of $6 a barrel) until 1987. Should Canada continue her present policy of importing half her domestic oil needs, proved southern reserves would last well into the 1990s. At a slightly higher price for oil (say, $8 a barrel) extensive tar sand development plus proved southern reserves would provide enough oil to meet total projected Canadian demand up to about the year 2000.

The key, then, to Ottawa's perplexing policy of speedy exploitation of the Arctic reserves lies not so much in any fear of a shortfall between domestic demand and production from southern reserves, as in the government's continuing policy of exporting as much oil and gas to the United States as possible. The more oil and gas made available in the Arctic, the more Canada can export without jeopardizing her own future supplies. Critics of this policy argue that Canada would be wiser, for the moment, to limit or eliminate petroleum exports and spend the money earmarked for immensely expensive Arctic transportation systems on development of other industrial sectors instead. The reserves could then be tapped at a more leisurely pace, in line with domestic requirements. They point out that while exports to the United States account for a substantial portion of Canadian production of oil and gas (about 50 per cent for both products in 1972), they fill only a tiny percentage of total U.S. needs. Canadian exports of oil to the United States in 1972 were about a million barrels a day, as compared with total U.S. daily consumption of 16 million barrels a day. Gas exports totalled about a trillion cubic feet during 1972, while total U.S. consumption amounted to about 24 trillion cubic feet. Thus it is argued that reduction or elimination of Canadian exports would have little significant impact on the United States, but would greatly extend potential Canadian self-sufficiency and delay the date when the need would arise to move into the Arctic. F. K. North, a professor of geology at Ottawa's Carleton University, has observed that, "If Canada could make the U.S. a gift of her total proven oil reserves—simply turn over to them every producing well in every field in Canada—we could extend the Americans' reserve life for oil by about 20 months." He asks:

> Are Canadians to pay billions of dollars to discover, produce and transport materials for use by peoples of another country; materials that Canadians themselves do not need [yet] but which their descendants will wish had been preserved for their use? Are Americans to be asked to pay for production and delivery systems that will lie

entirely in another nation's territory and be under that other nation's political control? Or are Canadians to surrender effective sovereignty over, say, twenty per cent of their territory, by allowing all the capital fixtures, all the ore carriers, all the ice-breaking LNG (liquefied natural gas) tankers, to be under the American flag?

The debate over these issues, which historians may well judge to have been among the most significant in the nation's history, has focused on the proposal of Canadian Arctic Gas (a consortium of sixteen American and eleven Canadian firms) for construction of a 2,600-mile-long Mackenzie Valley gas pipeline. Government hearings on the consortium's proposal began in March 1974 and were expected to extend over the following two years.

The pipeline, as planned by Arctic Gas, would begin at Prudhoe Bay in Alaska and snake its way southeast to Inuvik, where it would be joined by feeders from wells in the Mackenzie delta–Beaufort Sea region. From there it would stretch south to the Alberta border, where part of the gas would be channelled into the existing Alberta trunk system, which connects to markets in California. The new line would continue southward and then southeast across the prairies to Emerson, Manitoba, from where existing pipe would carry gas to the U.S. midwest and to central Canada. Estimated cost of the project (the largest construction job ever undertaken on earth) is $5.7 billion. Arctic Gas wants to begin construction in the winter of 1976-77: gas, they say, could then be flowing through the line by the fall of 1978. The ultimate capacity of the 48-inch line, to be reached by 1980-81, would be 4.5 billion cubic feet a day, of which about half a billion cubic feet would be consumed to power the system. Net yearly throughput would be about 1.5 trillion cubic feet. As proposed, half of this gas would come from Canadian wells and half would come from Prudhoe Bay.

By the time the line reached maximum throughput, then, Canada's gas production would have risen to about 4 trillion cubic feet a year (3.3 trillion from western Canada plus .7 billion from the north). Domestic demand in 1980 is projected to be about 2.5 trillion cubic feet. Because the line would have to operate at full capacity most of the time if it were to be economically feasible, this would mean that Canadian gas exports would have to be in the range of 1.5 trillion cubic feet, unless Alberta and British

Columbia, the main southern producers, could somehow be persuaded to cut back on their own exports. Not until 1990 would projected domestic Canadian demand for gas rise to meet domestic supply levels, allowing the pipeline to operate at full capacity without exports of Canadian gas to the United States. At that time, there will obviously be a need for more gas, if consumption is to be allowed to continue rising. But western provincial reserves will long ago have reached maximum output and slipped into decline because of falling well pressures, and Canada will be consuming her full 50 per cent share of the pipeline's 1.5 trillion cubic feet a year capacity. New frontier sources of supply will thus be needed.

Technical considerations involved in the production of Prudhoe Bay gas make it likely that total Canadian exports to the United States through the pipeline could be even higher than the figures above would indicate. While there is a huge amount of gas in the Prudhoe reservoir, perhaps 32 trillion cubic feet, it exists in two forms: a third of it is dissolved in oil, and two-thirds lies in a "gas cap" on top of the oil pool. The dissolved gas comes up automatically with the oil, and therefore can be fed directly into a gas pipeline. It presents no engineering problems. But the gas cap is what provides the pressure needed to get the oil out of the ground. Sound reservoir engineering dictates that this gas should not be tapped until the oil field has been in production for some time— perhaps ten years—if the maximum amount of oil is to be extracted. To try to maintain pressure by artificial means, such as by pumping sea water in, would seriously jeopardize the future of the reservoir. The Trans-Alaska oil pipeline is expected to be completed by 1977, and it will carry a maximum of about two million barrels a day to Valdez. There is about 800 cubic feet of gas in each barrel of oil, so until the Prudhoe gas cap is tapped, the amount of Prudhoe gas available for the Mackenzie Valley gas pipeline would be about 1.6 billion cubic feet a day. This means that, if the gas pipeline is to be run at capacity (4 billion cubic feet a day), the Mackenzie delta fields will have to supply 2.4 billion cubic feet a day for as long as seven years, or until the Prudhoe gas cap can be brought into production. Production in Canada would thus be even further out of line with domestic needs during these years, meaning that exports would have to be proportionately greater.

While it would appear from this that Canada's long-term interests would best be served by delaying construction of the pipeline at least until the late 1980s, Arctic Gas argues that this could be a costly option. Only by combining proved reserves of Prudhoe Bay gas (32 billion cubic feet) with those of the Mackenzie delta region (7 trillion cubic feet as of March, 1974) can enough gas be found to fill a 48-inch pipeline. And only by building a 48-inch pipeline (the largest diameter in use in North America) with its substantial economies of scale can transport costs be spread thinly enough over delivered volumes of gas to keep the price of the gas in southern markets down to about $1 a thousand cubic feet. A smaller-diameter pipeline, it is argued, could make Arctic gas too expensive for southern customers. As a corollary to this, it is pointed out that a group of U.S. companies is strongly advocating a pipeline for Prudhoe Bay gas across Alaska, parallel to the Trans-Alaska oil line. The gas would be liquefied and shipped to the U.S. west coast by tanker. This option would raise the price of Prudhoe Bay gas delivered to southern U.S. markets, but it would have the advantage, for security-conscious United States' interest groups, of being "all-American."

If this were to happen, Arctic Gas says, "when Canada sought to develop and use its Arctic reserves, it would be required to build a pipeline to serve its markets alone. This smaller volume pipeline would have much smaller economies of scale than a joint Canadian–U.S. gas pipeline. The result? Gas prices to Canadians would be very much higher, once an all-Canadian pipeline was ultimately built." This statement is correct only if two unstated premises are accurate. The first is that Canadian demand will never be big enough to fill a 48-inch pipeline; the second is that Canadian Arctic reserves will never be large enough to warrant long-term investment in such a line. However, Canadian demand will likely be big enough by about the end of the century, according to government projections, and the oil industry's own optimism would seem to support the belief that Mackenzie delta reserves will ultimately prove to be large enough to justify a 48-inch line on their own. In other words, the Arctic Gas statement would appear to be accurate only within a very short-term frame of reference.

Arctic Gas's most telling argument against a policy of Canadian self-sufficiency lies in the fact that such a policy would mean shutting off exports to the United States. Gas and oil exports from Canada are under the control of an autonomous National Energy Board, which examines requests for export permits and decides which ones should be accepted and which denied. It is charged with the responsibility of seeing that exports do not reach a level where future domestic supplies might fall short of domestic demand. Unfortunately, and by its own admission, the board has in the past relied on reserve estimates supplied by the oil and gas industry, estimates which have proved to be overly optimistic. The result has been that Canadian producers of gas had, by 1974, contractual agreements to supply U.S. customers with 15 trillion cubic feet of gas from western Canada over the following two decades. When these export commitments are added to domestic demand figures, the projected life of proved reserves in the south drops from eleven to about six years. (There is a certain irony in the fact that many of the companies involved in the Arctic Gas consortium are the same ones that had earlier convinced the National Energy Board that reserves were ample to permit large exports; these companies are now arguing that supplies are so short that the Mackenzie pipeline must be built immediately. The irony can be extended by observing once again that construction of the pipeline as proposed by the companies would mean increasing Canada's exports far beyond 1974 levels. The cycle could be continued *ad absurdum*.) Escape clauses contained in these export contracts give the National Energy Board the legal authority to revoke them. But Arctic Gas hints that the political repercussions of such action could be serious:

> Consider the following: Canada imports 20 million tons of U.S. coal annually to serve the energy needs of Ontario. Virtually all of the oil supplies for Ontario and about half its natural gas supplies are moved from western Canada by pipelines which extend in part across the United States. Every day Canadian consumers depend on these pipelines for nearly one billion cubic feet of natural gas and half a billion barrels of crude oil. In addition, refineries in Quebec depend upon a pipeline from Portland, Maine to deliver tank-imported crude oil across U.S. territory at a rate of several hundred thousand barrels a day.
>
> Beyond the field of energy, one quarter of our annual production as a nation is sold to foreigners. And 75 per cent of those exports are sold in the world's largest consumer market just south of us.

Given this situation it is in Canada's interest to preserve sound trading and financial relations. It is not in Canada's interest to abrogate its foreign commitments. . . .

To cancel gas export commitments already authorized by the government of Canada would be an act of irresponsibility; an act of self-delusion; an act of retrogression.

Eric Kierans, a former Liberal cabinet minister and one of the government's most acerbic critics on energy policy, has replied to this by stating:

I think of Ottawa in two ways, the capital of my country and the breeding-grounds of fears and haunting visions of what Washington might do. These constant bureaucratic nightmares make Ottawa less of a capital and Canada more of a satellite of the United States. Washington officials need only keep silent and Ottawa's terror at what the United States might do will do their work for them. The Americans serve their purpose best when they keep quiet.

Let the rest of the country not be caught in the Ottawa den of dread, awe and reverence and [instead] look at the facts. There are three things Washington knows about our energy policy. First, that it is Canadian policy, stated a thousand times, to export only excess reserves. Secondly, that Parliament created a National Energy Board precisely to secure and ensure adequate reserves for Canadian consumption needs now and in the future. Thirdly, that Parliament placed in the National Energy Board Act, section 17 which states: "The board may review, rescind, change, alter or vary any order or decision" made by it.

In the end, however, no amount of academic debate will answer the question of whether, and in what ways, Washington might retaliate for interruption of Canadian gas exports. The field of diplomacy is not one that lends itself to rational analysis and prediction.

There is a further area of concern for Canadians in the Mackenzie Valley pipeline debate, and that is whether the country has the financial strength to undertake a $5.7 billion construction project over five years without suffering serious disruptions to established sectors of the economy. This becomes particularly worrying when it is realized that Quebec's James Bay hydro project could be at its peak investment phase at the same time as pipeline construction is getting underway. The James Bay project could cost a total of $6 billion — more, even, than the pipeline.

Since Canada's entire GNP will amount to only about $170 billion by the late 1970s, clearly some of the capital will have to come from outside Canada.

The federal Department of Energy, Mines and Resources study, *An Energy Policy for Canada*, states the problem this way:

> Different concerns have been expressed that the large projects now under consideration will unduly strain the country's resources, thereby creating inflation and serious dislocation of markets over the shorter term, especially if there is any bunching of the projects. From a longer term perspective, there is a general apprehension that there will be a significant resource reallocation to the energy sector which would . . . not be consistent with Canada's socio-economic priorities. A particular concern often voiced is that, because large foreign capital inflows will be required to finance these projects, and because some of the projects would be oriented to servicing U.S. markets, there would be strong upward pressure on the exchange rate [the Canadian dollar would increase in value relative to the American dollar]. A higher value for the Canadian dollar is held to be bad for the country as it would lead to a deterioration in the competitive positions of Canadian export and import-competing industries, particularly in the manufacturing sector. It is thought that the consequent loss of jobs in these industries might even be greater than the increased employment opportunities associated with the energy projects. A sometimes corollary to this argument is that the government should act to limit primary resource development and drive down the exchange value of the Canadian dollar in order to create a climate conducive to increased growth in the manufacturing sector. In turn, it is held that this would provide the required employment opportunities for Canada's fast growing and highly qualified labour force.

Using computer models of the Canadian economy, the study analysed the impact of five different sets of policy options in the area of energy development (all of which implicitly contained the capital requirements of the James Bay project):

CASE A: SELF-SUFFICIENT DEVELOPMENT

It assumes:

a) the maintenance of currently authorized natural gas exports only;

b) the export of crude oil not to surpass imports of oil for Canadian needs;

c) the construction of a Mackenzie Valley natural gas pipline not to begin this decade;
d) the moderate development of eastern offshore gas and oil to begin in 1975;
e) the continuation of the present rate of conventional (western Canadian) oil and gas development through to 1975 and then a marked decline (due to declining reserves); and
f) limited oil sand developments.

Total capital expenditure in this decade (1970-1980) is estimated, for this case, to be about $42 billion current, requiring an 8.2 per cent annual average rate of growth compared with the average rate over the last decade of 10.7 per cent. (Capital expenditure could be increased by investment in non-energy sectors of the economy.)

CASE B: STANDARD DEVELOPMENT

It assumes:

a) the construction of a Mackenzie Valley natural gas pipeline to begin in 1975, and for Mackenzie delta natural gas to reach markets by 1978;
b) the development of eastern offshore gas and oil to begin in 1975;
c) the continuation of the present rate of conventional gas and oil development through to 1975 and then a gradual decline; and
d) the gradual increase of oil sand developments.

Total capital expenditure in this decade is estimated at about $50 billion under this case, requiring an average 10.1 per cent rate of growth. Because of the peaking of expenditures in 1976 and the sudden drop thereafter, the average annual rate of growth is lower than the 10.7 per cent historical growth rate.

CASE C: DELAYED DEVELOPMENT

Case c is similar to Case b with the following exceptions:

a) the delay in the development of the Mackenzie Valley gas and oil production capacity; and
b) the construction of the Mackenzie Valley gas pipeline is assumed to begin in 1977 rather than 1975.

51

Total capital requirement for Case c is expected to be about $49 billion, requiring an 11 per cent annual rate of growth.

CASE D: EXTENSIVE DEVELOPMENT

In addition to the development noted under Case B, it assumes:
a) the development of Arctic offshore oil and gas production capacity;
b) a Mackenzie Valley gas pipeline with construction in 1978–79 and some pipeline construction offshore and from Ellesmere Island;
c) oil production projects on Ellesmere Island and in the Mackenzie delta to reach markets by the end of this decade, and
d) some additional oil sands and refinery developments.

Total capital investment in this decade is expected to amount to about $60 billion under this case, requiring an average 13½ per cent annual rate of growth.

CASE E: MAXIMUM DEVELOPMENT

In addition to developments noted in Cases B and D, it assumes:
a) the development of a uranium enrichment plant starting in 1977;
b) additional oil and gas production capacity on Ellesmere Island and in the Mackenzie delta and offshore;
c) maximum development of oil sands potential and the expansion of refining capacity;
d) more development on the east coast and the development of Beaufort Sea and the Arctic islands areas at the end of the decade; and
e) additional gas pipeline developments in the Arctic islands and Beaufort Sea.

Total capital expenditures in this decade are estimated to be over $68 billion in this case, requiring a 17½ per cent annual average rate of growth.

In commenting on these scenarios, the government study rules out both the extensive and maximum development cases as having "quite unsatisfactory" ramifications for the economy in terms of inflation and unemployment. The standard development case, it says, could be undertaken without serious disruptions in the economy, particularly if it got underway during a period of recession or slowdown in the economy. If the economy were already operating at close to full capacity, there would be some short-term inflation, and the net positive effect on employment would be minimal. The delayed development case would have the advantage of placing the stresses of development on a somewhat larger economic base, thus smoothing out some of the bumps in the growth chart. But both the standard and delayed development cases, it should be remembered, involve a long-term commitment to extensive exports of Canadian gas to U.S. markets.

The self-sufficiency case does not involve this commitment, and therefore it would permit a greater degree of flexibility in questions of choosing the optimum growth rate for the country's economy and deciding which sectors of the economy should be developed to maximize social benefits. A broader range of options would remain open to planners.

According to the study, "The possible advocacy of a policy of self-sufficiency does not envisage any [necessary] slowdown in economic growth as a result of reduced resource exploitation, but in fact suggests that the goal of long-term economic growth can be most effectively met by choosing the self-sufficiency route." Adoption of the self-sufficiency policies, or some variation of them, would thus seem to be in Canada's best interest, in both the long term and the short term.

Whether this view of the national interest will prevail in the decision as to whether to allow Arctic Gas to begin construction on the Mackenzie Valley pipeline is problematical. The application is being heard by the National Energy Board, which is composed mainly of engineers and accountants, and whose track record, as has been seen, is far from perfect. Their decision will need the approval of cabinet; the present Liberal government has repeatedly stated its enthusiasm for the project. And there are other considerations tilting the scales in favour of Arctic Gas's application or, more generally, in favour of any application for northern development. One is the mystical, unquestioning, devotion to growth that Canada holds in common with virtually every other industrial nation. Another has to do with the particular bureaucratic organization of the government department responsible for overseeing the development of the north. The Department of Indian Affairs and Northern Development (DIAND) has virtually complete control over northern land use. The Department of the Environment is given no share of decision-making authority; it is expected to act as an adviser, but only when invited by DIAND to do so.

DIAND's work is divided into three categories, the first and preeminent of which is Northern Economic Development. This section administers land use in the north, including exploration permits and mining and drilling leases, and generally exercises all the authority of a provincial government where resource management, social and environmental programs are concerned. Its director is also a member of the board of directors of Panarctic Oils. The second section, Indian and Eskimo Affairs, has national responsibility for guardianship of native peoples. In this role it is obliged to do its best to alleviate social problems of natives in the north. Many of these problems—the disintegration of native communities, the destruction of local, self-sustaining hunting, fishing and trapping economies and resultant unemployment— have resulted from past policies of rapid development of the north. Indian and Eskimo Affairs would in theory seem to have a clear responsibility to try to moderate the rate of economic growth in the north; in fact, however, its decision-making is dominated by Northern Economic Development. The Conservation branch of the department has responsibility for Canada's national parks and historic sites, including those in the north. Occasions when the Conservation branch and not Northern Economic Development decides where a northern park will be located are rare and generally well-publicized as a victory for conservationists.

Each of the three men directing these sections reports to a deputy minister who, like the Northern Economic Development director, is also a member of the board of Panarctic Oils. The deputy minister, of course, is responsible to the elected minister, who must somehow represent all three divisions in cabinet discussions.

The Canadian Arctic Resources Committee, a respected group of conservation-oriented academics who have pooled their talents to examine and publicize northern development issues, has commented on this arrangement:

> The result is that one branch of government has a power over northern lands roughly similar to that of a feudal lord. The power of Northern Economic Development in respect to its given purpose is unequalled by any other important branch of government in Canada. The development ethic is the sole value and goal of the Northern Economic Development branch, which may be quite proper for the branch, since this is its stated and intended function. But where are the checks and balances? Is this approach truly reflective of the values of the Canadian electorate? Moreover, when the government becomes the exploring party, as with Panarctic Oils, the force and control are monolithic and awesome. The regulated and regulators are the same.

Perhaps the most striking case of conflict of interest to arise out of this bureaucratic spider's web concerns construction of the Mackenzie Highway, a 1,060-mile all-weather road from the Alberta border to Inuvik, near the rim of the Beaufort Sea. The highway is being built, in part, to facilitate pipeline construction down the river valley. It was begun in April 1972, immediately after plans were made public by the prime minister. The announcement took most government departments (but not DIAND) completely by surprise. Much of the routing and clearing of the first fifty miles from Fort Simpson to Camsell Bend was done during the summer of 1972, in what could only be described as a headlong rush. The government ignored its own land use regulations, even to the extent of using bulldozers in the summer months, when areas of permafrost are most vulnerable to damage. One result has been development of a number of land slump erosion areas in and along the right-of-way. It soon became apparent that no study of the environmental impact of highway construction had been undertaken until construction was well under way; public indignation over this fact, along with unforeseen construction problems, forced the government to halt work on the road for a year, nine months after it had begun, to allow time for environmental studies to be completed. Since then, hand-clearing of much of the right-of-way has been finished (with the exception of an area around Wrigley, at mile 435). The result of this episode has been to increase public cynicism over government claims to a concern for environmental protection which would balance its commitment to economic development. But it has also served to increase public awareness of the shortcoming of the existing departmental structure.

Further conflict-of-interest problems can be expected to arise out of the question of native land claims in territories through which the Mackenzie River flows. Indian claims to ownership of lands covered by Treaties 8 and 11 (which include the entire northern half of the Mackenzie pipeline right-of-way) were reinforced by the courts in 1973, when Justice William Morrow of the Supreme Court of the Northwest Territories granted the Northwest Territories Indian Brotherhood a caveat; as long as it remains standing, its effect will be to prevent the granting of clear title to lands needed for pipeline construction without the agreement of the Indians. This has given the natives a strong bargaining position in land settlement negotiations with the federal government, which is anxious to proceed with development.

Wrigley is a small Indian settlement on the east bank of the Mackenzie River, about halfway between Great Slave Lake and Great Bear Lake in the Northwest Territories. It is also on the route of the northern extension of the Mackenzie Highway which is being built by the federal government as a prelude to work on the Mackenzie Valley gas pipeline. What follows is an excerpt from minutes of a meeting of the settlement council on September 11, 1973 (three months before highway construction was temporarily halted to allow time for environmental impact statements to be prepared).

PROJECT MANAGER, MACKENZIE HIGHWAY: I would like to say how pleased I am to be here to talk to you about the highway. I brought a map, and if you'll allow me I'll put it up here so I can talk about this map. It's a map showing the settlement of Wrigley, the river, and the mountains, and possible places for the highway. I'd like to put it up here if I may.

CHAIRMAN: If they want to work on the highway it's up to the people of Fort Wrigley to say where we want it, and if we want it. If we say no, they're not going to work on it.

MANAGER: (explains that his purpose is only to discuss alternative routes, not whether or not the highway should be built.)

CHAIRMAN: What do you feel about it? If you like it you should say so, or if you don't, you should say so. If you want to say no, we can all agree with you. It's our land, and whatever we say, the government should abide by it.

COUNCILLOR HARDISTY: We have already discussed this highway and the problems we're going to have, like disturbances to the community, liquor, fighting, prostitution, more Whites, development being taken over by the Whites. What does the rest of the council want? Do you want a highway or not? I think I don't like the idea of the highway to the community.

COUNCILLOR NAYALLY: We all agree that we don't want the highway.

COUNCILLOR TALE: I agree with what Councillor Nayally says.

COUNCILLOR HARDISTY: The Manager says the alternative route, one further from the community by one and a half miles, would cost the government too much money; then why have the highway through at all? If they forget the whole highway that's okay with me. A lot of the time we say no to the government, but they disapprove of what people are saying. In Judge Morrow's court decision (establishing the validity of aboriginal land claims) there were certain rules, but the government still keeps pushing us. We don't like that. If we say no, that's our decision. We don't want the same thing to happen to us that happened to the Fort Simpson people, being exploited and all the rest.

MANAGER: What if the highway bypasses the settlement without an extension to the settlement?

COUNCILLOR HARDISTY: Even if there's no extension to this settlement we do not know what the settlement north of us thinks about the highway. It's also up to the people north of us if they want a highway or not. But we don't want it anyway.

CHAIRMAN: Even if the highway bypasses the settlement north of us by five miles we don't know what they will think.

MANAGER: Mr. Chairman, would it make any difference to you, if there is a highway, and if it were one and a half miles away instead of half a mile? You would see less of a highway if it were one and a half miles away; you wouldn't see much dust and there would be much less of an impact if it were over there.

COUNCILLOR HARDISTY: We're saying we don't want the highway and we don't know what the people north of us are saying. All this discussion will get nowhere. We just don't want the highway—period.

MANAGER: May I ask then, Mr. Chairman, if you are interested at all in any of the benefits such as being able to operate garages, cafes on the highway, if there is one . . .

BAND CHIEF HORESAY: The manager is talking about the benefits the people will have if the highway comes. One of the tricks of the government used to be to fool the Indians. A lot of time they use those tricks to fool the people of the north. And this time they are not going to do that to us.

COUNCILLOR HARDISTY: With cafes and garages, they say we are going to make money from the highway. If we have a cafe without the highway, we can still make money. There are a lot of tourists going north by the river; the *Norweta* goes up and down the river and tourists stop at the settlement. If we have a coffee shop here they will go to it and eat and buy crafts. Without the highway we can still make money.

MANAGER: Mr. Chairman, if there were tourists on the highway they could come into the settlement but you would rather have them not come in at all. Is that what you mean? You would rather have no access from the highway at all to the settlement?

COUNCILLOR HARDISTY: We are not saying that we don't want the tourists going down the river. We are saying we don't want the highway. Whatever the White men do on the river, going up or down, it's not our business. What we are here for is to talk about the highway, not tourists.

MANAGER: Well, would the half mile be too close, or is one and a half miles still too close, Mr. Chairman?

CHAIRMAN: We are not saying half a mile is too close, or how many miles we want the highway. We are saying we just *don't want* the highway.

COUNCILLOR HARDISTY: With the highway we will have disturbance to the animals . . . they will disappear or be destroyed.

MANAGER: Mr. Chairman, we have people, environmental people and people who are knowledgeable about game, who are working with us to ensure that game will not be disturbed. The idea is to design the highway so we do not disturb the game.

COUNCILLOR TALE: We agree that we don't want the highway.

MANAGER: If it were farther away from the settlement, then it would disturb you less; would this not be better?

COUNCILLOR NAYALLY: We just can't say whether or not we want the highway. There are a lot of other people that live along the Mackenzie River who will be affected by the highway. We don't know what the people north of us are thinking; we don't want the highway, but we can't speak for those people.

MANAGER: So you want to discuss this with the people at Fort Norman and Good Hope and the other settlement, is that what you are saying?

COUNCILLOR HARDISTY: What does the council think? Should we wait until another meeting with other settlements?

MANAGER: Mr. Chairman, does this mean you want to speak to the people at Fort Norman, or are you suggesting that we should speak to the people of Fort Norman as well?

COUNCILLOR HARDISTY: If the government goes down to visit other settlements and have meetings with the people, they are not going to come back with the exact answers that the other settlements give. They will just give us what the government is thinking . . . the Manager says if the highway by-passes Fort Wrigley by five miles it will not bother the settlement; but in the future they will make an extension to Fort Wrigley because there's a lot of activity and exploration across (the river) from us. They have found some minerals across there, and for sure they are going to put an extension road to the settlement. They can't always use planes. We will have another meeting soon between ourselves and other natives and we will make one decision and we will meet again. Right now the manager is giving us so many alternatives that if he keeps this up we may give in. So think about it.

MANAGER: Mr. Chairman, may I say there is no need to have a road into Wrigley at all if you don't want one? Secondly, may I say something about the planning of a highway and the time it will take in order for the highway to get here? Starting right from today it would probably be three years before there would be a highway even close to Wrigley. And if it did come close there would be no need to have an access into Wrigley from the highway if you didn't want one.

CHAIRMAN: What does the council think? Do you want the highway on your land or not? If you don't want them on your land, just tell them.

BAND CHIEF HORESAY: We don't want it on our land. That is what we are saying.

COUNCILLOR NAYALLY: In the past we didn't have the highway, and our forefathers survived. They hunted on this land and fished without the highway. We can survive too.

MANAGER: Mr. Chairman, does this mean that you're saying that no one from Wrigley would like to either have a garage connected with the highway, or a cafe, or to be involved in maintaining a highway or looking after a highway, looking after the roadbed to make sure that it is kept well? Does this mean that no one in Fort Wrigley would like to take any part at all either now or in the future?

COUNCILLOR HARDISTY: Our land is our land. If they keep this up, on and on, back to the same thing over and over, we will still say no and that's it. *We don't want it.* We are not saying that with the highway we are going to make money in the cafe or in the garage or looking after the highway. We know there are going to be a lot of problems with the highway, and that is why we are saying we just don't want it.

MANAGER: I suppose what I'm saying, Mr. Chairman, is that there's lots of time, because there's three years before the highway would come close to Wrigley. There is time for you to decide how to be involved in it, whether you would like to be involved in maintaining it or camps and guides for tourists, or any such thing. You would have time in the next three years to think about it and train yourselves or get training or funds to help you in organizing yourselves to do this.

CHAIRMAN: If they put the highway in there will be more boozing, more trouble-makers, and more deaths due to drinking.

MANAGER: Well, Mr. Chairman, you are quite correct. These things can happen but it is our job to plan this highway so that there are few accidents, so that there is no booze, so that you are not troubled by those problems. That is part of our job and we are prepared to help in any way we can, and we have some time in which to do it.

CHAIRMAN: We still don't know what the people of Fort Norman, Norman Wells, Good Hope, McPherson are thinking about the highway, so we can't open the highway through here.

MANAGER: In closing, Mr. Chairman, I would like to say one thing. I can safely say that we are prepared to spend more time and money working with people and the land to ensure that this highway is built better than any other highway has ever been built in the north. Mr. Chairman, the most important part of all in the building of the highway is that we build one that suits the people of the settlements, such as this one and Fort Norman and Good Hope.

CHAIRMAN: (aside) What are you thinking? Is he right or is he wrong?

COUNCILLOR HARDISTY: We said no, and that's it. If we say yes to the highway, we are saying yes to the pipeline and opening up for White men.

BAND CHIEF HORESAY: That's right.

COUNCILLOR HARDISTY: If we don't want the pipeline, that means we don't want the highway either. If we open either one of them, we are opening both. That is why they keep at us with the highway. There has been a lot of oil activity around our area and all they want is to connect the pipeline to it. They will make money on it and we will make nothing out of it. If we say yes to the highway, we are just buggering up our land.

Following the discussion, Wrigley Council passed the following resolution: "Council agrees that the Mackenzie Highway must not be constructed by Fort Wrigley at this time and that the people of this settlement are not in the least way prepared to meet the tremendous impact which it will bring." The struggle continues, but in the north—even more than elsewhere—it is apparent that "you can't beat City Hall".

Farther north, at Fort Good Hope (mile 725 on the proposed Mackenzie Highway), the council objected to establishment of a federal Department of Public Works portable Arctic construction camp nearby at the Rabbitskin River. However, majority approval of the council was eventually obtained and the camp, designed to be self-sufficient and thereby to have a minimal impact on neighbouring communities, was put in place in November 1973. One of the two objecting members on the six-person council, Lucy Jackson, expressed her disapproval this way:

I have already told Council that for me to make a decision on any-thing that had to do with this town and people, I have to think about it. I cannot make a decision then and there. How will our people benefit from this and will it be good for our people? I feel that I am in the Council for the people. To vote or to make a motion on an important matter we have to have our people's opinion. It is not my right for me just to say yes. Why do we always have to make our motion right there? Shouldn't we be allowed to think about it? This is not a little, unimportant thing: this involves our town and our people. This involves everyone, young boys and also old mothers.

We know and I know the local boys will be hired, but for how long? A week? A month? And then one or two of them will get drunk and pretty soon they will not be working. Why? They'll tell us: too much drinking. And then, who gets hired? More people from outside. We really do have, and still have, drinking problems. So those guys will not be helped much there.

Take last year, those thirty men from the Department of Energy, Mines and Resources and Poole Construction workers. Weren't they drinking and controlling the town all summer? Even when you went in to the dances, they were all over. So how can you say it's all right? Last year nobody tried to make rules or set limits for them. Will it be like that again? Last year they stayed "only" four months. And this year you, the council, say "only" eighteen months.

What is happening to us, to our children? We, the parents, the people of this land, have a say in this. What will happen to our girls in town? No doubt the men will be looking for them first. And what happens? You well know. And it's not the girls' fault. It's going to be excitement for them. Well, who isn't looking for excitement when they're young? In the old days, the older people always looked after the children. It is not like that any more. Why? Because maybe everything is changing so much, going too fast for them. . . .

To my eyes, it's like everyone is being led by a string to say yes to this and yes to that. For myself, I have to look into the matter widely, not only for today, but for years to come, to know the good and bad points.

How do we know they will not do damage down at Rabbitskin River? We used that as a picnic area and for fishing in the summer, for catching loche in the winter and for many other things which you think are useless. But from the beginning of time we made use of everything even though to you it was useless.

The government people have been saying lately that the native people should get back to the traditional ways. So why put these people right in our town with all of their equipment? You tell us we can teach the children our language and our culture. How will the children feel when they see this and us trying to teach them our ways?

3.
The Alberta Tar Sands

Times change. In 1729 Jonathan Swift wrote "A Modest Proposal," in which he suggested the eating of babies as a solution to both famine and overpopulation. The work was regarded by his contemporaries, as it is today, as a bitingly ironic social satire. For nearly 250 years, people have been reading the essay and laughing in spite of themselves. In our own era, Herman Kahn of the Hudson Institute, the famous American think tank, writes books in which he suggests ways in which the United States could go about "winning" a thermonuclear war. One of his books is called *Thinking About the Unthinkable*; others are *On Thermonuclear War* and *On Escalation*. Kahn has achieved wide recognition and much respect, not as a satirist, but as a social engineer and futurologist, and he is often consulted by powerful government officials. Few people laugh when they read his books, even though their implicit morality (or rather, amorality) is no less outrageous than that of "A Modest Proposal."

Late in 1973, Herman Kahn travelled to Ottawa, where he met with Prime Minister Pierre Trudeau, his minister of energy Donald Macdonald and a few top advisors. At that meeting he presented Mr. Trudeau and the others with a plan that was, in its own way, as grotesque as anything he has had to suggest with regard to winning nuclear wars: his idea was to solve the "free world's" energy shortage by investing $15 to $20 billion of international money in a crash program to build twenty oil-processing plants by 1980 in Alberta's Athabasca tar sands region. The plants, fed by massive strip-mining operations, would ultimately produce two million barrels of synthetic tar sand crude oil a day, and Kahn's plans called for all of it to be exported to the United States, Japan and Western Europe. Between 1978 and 1984 six billion barrels would be siphoned off for export. To meet the fantastic labour requirements of such a scheme, Kahn proposed that 30,000 to 40,000 South Korean coolies be shipped to Alberta for the construction phase. Acknowledging that no one had yet devised an environmentally sound method of disposing of the oily, chemical-laden waste water tailings of tar sands processing plants, Kahn suggested they be simply dumped into the Athabasca, one of the world's great, historic rivers, and that the river be written off as a sewer for five million cubic yards of liquid tailings a day.

Since Kahn specifically requested that his proposals be given no immediate publicity, we have no public record of how his audience reacted at that Ottawa meeting. Things being what they are these days, one can assume that no one actually laughed in his face, though we are told by one reporter who seems to know that the energy minister, at least, was "underwhelmed." And later on, the Alberta environment minister told an oil sands conference in Edmonton that such instant development of the Athabasca sands would result in social and economic chaos, beginning with "a population increase in Alberta of half a million people, a 30 per cent increase, in just a few years. This would require an equivalent increase in housing, in schools, hospitals and health services generally, and recreation facilities." There would be "major and chronic shortages of services, goods and materials, and general increasing inflation, labour strife, and general instability to a degree that a major citizens' backlash would no doubt occur."

Still, weeks after the Ottawa meeting, Canadians were treated to the perplexing spectacle of the federal minister of supply and services—the government's quartermaster—stumping the West giving speeches on energy policy in which he advocated a scheme for rapid development of the Athabasca tar sands which sounded suspiciously like Kahn's. Canada would stand to make profits of $2 to $3 billion a year, he argued. Asked to explain why the minister, Jean-Pierre Goyer, was invading the territory of his cabinet colleague, the minister of energy, and whether his suggestions reflected federal policy on the tar sands, Prime Minister Trudeau replied only that, yes, Mr. Goyer had his permission to speak on the subject but, no, his suggestions did not reflect government policy.

This peculiar, unexplained episode was a strange contrast to the early history of sabotage and obstruction surrounding development of the fabulously rich oil sands deposits in northern Alberta, which are estimated to contain better than 900 billion barrels of raw bitumen, from which 26.5 billion barrels of high-quality crude oil can be recovered by strip mining and processing and another 80 to 150 billion barrels by the less efficient "in situ" recovery methods used to exploit the deeper deposits. With substantial improvements in recovery technology, the tar sands might ultimately yield considerably more oil than this, perhaps as much as 250 billion barrels in total, according to Alberta government estimates. In other words, about a third of the world's known petroleum reserves lie locked up in the Alberta sands, which is reason enough to account for all manner of intrigue.

The father of commercial crude oil production from the Athabasca tar sands is R. C. Fitzsimmons, a pioneer referred to only briefly, if at all, in official histories of the sands. It was in 1922 that Fitzsimmons first went to Fort McMurray to investigate rumours about the prodigious oil wealth of the tar sand deposits in the area. Encouraged by what he saw, he subsequently purchased leases on nearly six thousand acres of rich tar sand land about fifty miles north of the town, a plot he later named Bitumount. By 1925 he had set up a small plant which produced oil by mixing the sand with hot water. Clean sand fell to the bottom of the kettle and the oil floated to the top, where it could be skimmed off. Tests carried out on the oil thus produced showed that it would make a high-quality refinery feedstock, and in 1927 Fitzsimmons formed the International Bitumen Company under a federal charter, convinced that his fortune had been made. The next two years were occupied with highly secret exploration of the leases and experimentation with oil extraction methods; Fitzsimmons and his crew told anyone who asked what they were up to that they were prospecting. By 1930 Fitzsimmons had decided that it was not feasible to extract the oil in situ by heating the sand beneath the surface of the earth with steam and pumping it to the surface, so he focused his attention on construction of a small hot-water plant based on the method he had worked out in 1925. By the end of the season, 340 barrels of pure crude oil had been extracted, cleaned and dehydrated. So effective had been the secrecy surrounding the venture that the people of Fort McMurray discovered that an extraction plant was in operation only when the first shipment of oil was barged up the Athabasca for shipment to Edmonton in the fall of 1930. The company applied for and was granted a patent on the extraction method worked out by Fitzsimmons.

The following year a new, larger plant was built. It had a capacity of 200 barrels a single shift, but it had to be shut down after producing only 2,000 barrels. Fitzsimmons had run into the first of the roadblocks that were to plague his company almost from the day it proved commercial exploitation of the vast tar sands reserves to be feasible. The problem this time was that no market could be found for the oil, which was being offered by the company as prime material for asphalt paving, roofing, waterproofing and so on. Potential purchasers were wary of the tar sands oil because it required slightly different processing than conventional crude; so most of the year's production had to be given away in an attempt to acquaint buyers with its potential. A few miles of road in Banff and Medicine Hat were paved with asphalt made from the oil, with results that were completely acceptable, and a Calgary roofing company marketed a whole range of products based on the oil they had been given by International Bitumen. But buyers still insisted that the oil meet conventional crude oil product specifications before they would commit themselves to purchases.

This meant a refinery would have to be constructed to break down the crude bitumen extracted from the sand into "specification" products. In a reminiscence published in 1953, Fitzsimmons recounted the frustrations of trying to raise money to build that refinery. His first attempt involved a share issue in Montreal, which was all but finalized when the Alberta government published an "official" description of development in the tar sands which made no mention of the International Bitumen operation, despite the fact that it was the first company ever to extract oil from the sands in commercial quantities. The government report was widely distributed, and the share issue fell through when brokers became wary of dealing with a company whose name did not even appear in the document. Further attempts to raise funds in London and Chicago looked promising until the lenders contacted the Alberta government for confirmation of the International Bitumen operation and either failed to receive any reply or received replies that appeared vague and evasive. Finally, however, the company did manage to raise most of the money it needed, and in anticipation of construction of the refinery, the extraction plant was expanded in 1936 to a capacity of 350 barrels a day.

By the fall of 1937 the refinery had been completed, but it failed to work satisfactorily. A justifiable paranoia setting in, Fitzsimmons recalls that "we had reason to believe that the trouble was by design rather than by error." Plot or no plot, money had to be found to fund redesign and repair work, and in November of 1937 Fitzsimmons travelled to Chicago to look for backers. Friends there put him in touch with a group in Boston which was willing to put up $300,000 subject to confirmation of the company's reports on its operations. Once again, the deal collapsed when the Alberta government in the person of the then deputy minister of trade and industry sent the Boston group what purported to be a complete history of tar sands exploration and development work which made no mention of International Bitumen. According to Fitzsimmons, the American financiers believed the company's reports but were nonetheless convinced that the provincial government "definitely was doublecrossing our company."

So in 1938, Fitzsimmons reports, "we went ahead without money." The defects in the refinery were corrected, and during a short production run 4,500 barrels of specification asphalt and 2,000 barrels of fuel oil were produced. But again, they could find no market, even though the products met industry specifications. Fitzsimmons reported in his article that potential buyers told him they had been warned by major conventional suppliers—the big, established oil companies—that if they purchased product from International Bitumen they would be cut off from conventional supplies. Since the buyers could not be certain of receiving all the product they needed from International Bitumen, they were forced to stick with the big companies.

If International Bitumen was to provide assurance of continued supplies expensive storage facilities would have to be erected, and the extraction plant and refinery would have to be further expanded. In debt, but sitting on a potential gold mine, the company tried for the next three years to raise the necessary money, with no success. In 1942 the fervently free enterprise

Social Credit government of William (Bible Bill) Aberhart was approached with a request for $50,000 either as an outright loan or as an advance on payment for asphalt. It seemed a modest request, since it would have put the company back in business supplying petroleum products which were by then in tight, wartime supply. And at that time—in fact, until 1949—Canada was importing more than 95 per cent of its petroleum requirements. Asphalt was selling for $12 a barrel and the plant was capable of producing 500 barrels a day in a single shift; it would thus have taken International Bitumen less than three months to pay the government back out of production. But the government refused the loan.

The frustrated Fitzsimmons could only conclude that there was a deliberate conspiracy to keep the tar sands out of production. The obstruction, he observed, "seemed to follow a well defined pattern on the part of both the [federal] and the Albertan provincial governments, regardless of which party was in power, which means that both were subject to the same pressure groups." Those pressure groups, he suggests, were the major oil companies, who did not want to see their huge investments in conventional oilfields around the world undercut by the opening up of the Athabasca reserves.

In any case, International Bitumen, blocked from access to both financial and commercial markets, was by 1942 impotent and ripe for a takeover by anyone who had the access they lacked. And into the company's offices that fall strode Mr. L. R. Champion of St. James Street, Montreal, a man unknown to Fitzsimmons but well known to the Alberta cabinet and to its minister of lands and minerals, Nathan E. Tanner. Champion offered to take over the company and put it on a sound financial footing, and after protracted negotiations, Fitzsimmons accepted the offer. It was a move he was soon to regret.

A new company was formed, Oil Sands Limited, which early in 1943 took over all the assets and liabilities of International Bitumen, including the patent on tar sands oil extraction it held. Shareholders were given one share in the new firm for every five shares they held in International Bitumen, and Champion took majority control. Over the following months, Fitzsimmons watched his dreams of getting his plant back into production crumble as it became clear to him that Champion had no intention of putting the operation on a commercial footing. The final straw was the apparent sabotaging of the new refinery late in 1944. Meanwhile, Fitzsimmons learned that Champion had hired an engineer to design a completely new extraction plant based on the original design. He was dumbfounded by the move, since the new plant was to be only a small, non-commercial prototype facility, and the old one was perfectly capable of fulfilling that role as it stood. Unable to get the answers he requested about the new plant, and unable to get Champion-hired men to cooperate in starting up the old plant, Fitzsimmons resigned as plant manager and left Bitumount in disgust and for the last time in September, 1944.

Two months later Champion incorporated a new company, Bitumount Holding Company, with him and his wife as the only shareholders. He then arranged for Oil Sands Limited to trade its rich surface deposits, extraction plant, refinery, living quarters and other improvements to the new holding company in return for some other oil sands leases Champion held which were covered by two hundred feet of overburden and thus not suitable even for sophisticated strip mining. Oil Sands did, however, retain possession of the extraction patent.

Champion's next move was even more surprising. On December 4, 1944, he pledged all of Bitumount Holding Company's newly acquired property—the surface deposits, the refinery, the extraction plant—to the Alberta government in an agreement under which Oil Sands would build a new pilot extraction plant at Bitumount with government money, retaining an option to buy the completed plant. The board set up to supervise construction included Champion, Tanner (the minister of lands and mines) and another cabinet minister. Four years after the deal had been signed the Alberta government took complete control of the new extraction plant and all of Bitumount's former holdings when Champion failed to meet his obligations under the agreement.

Fitzsimmons, charging bribery and other illegalities had been involved in the agreement between Champion and the Alberta government, launched court action against Champion and Oil Sands Limited in June 1945. The case was brought to an effective standstill when the government seized all of the company records of International Bitumen and held them for three and a half years, until the ultimate foreclosure on Champion's interest in the new extraction plant at Bitumount.

The Alberta government's research council subsequently was to operate the new extraction plant only very briefly as a pilot project. In 1950 the government agency reported that commercial extraction operations seemed to be feasible and the following year the first Athabasca Oil Sands conference was held in Edmonton to acquaint the oil industry with the government's leasing policy and to sell leases to interested firms.

No investigation was ever held into the peculiar circumstances surrounding Fitzsimmons' frustrating attempts to set up a commercial extraction plant and the role of Champion, Tanner and the Alberta government in squeezing the Athabasca pioneer out of what appears to have been a promising enterprise. In 1955 Fitzsimmons' written report on the events was tabled in the Alberta legislature by an MLA who was later to become a justice of the Alberta Supreme Court, but no discussion or examination of the document ever took place because the premier unexpectedly dissolved the House the next morning. Later a provincial government commission of inquiry into aspects of the oil industry refused to examine the report on grounds that it had no authority to consider matters not specifically referred to it by the provincial cabinet. The 1958 federal Royal Commission on Energy also refused to examine the question, stating in its baffling response to inquiries that Fitzsimmons' report "does not seem to come within our terms of reference. In other words, it is not related to problems of the export of, or sources of, energy."

Fitzsimmons stated his own conclusions clearly in 1953: "You may find it hard to believe that the tar sands were purposely kept out of production . . . unless you understand that the major oil companies must have oil reserves so that they know 30 to 50 years ahead where their next source of supply is coming from. Consequently they spend millions of dollars searching for new fields, but the tar sands was one source of supply that they did not have to search for and they were determined to have that held in reserve until all [conventional] oil fields ran low, when they would open up that area. Which, according to their plans, may be another 20 to 30 years." From the perspective of 1974's energy crisis, this seems a prophetic judgment.

Champion's Oil Sands Limited (now sporting a retired Alberta cabinet minister on its board of directors) was eventually to sell a licence to use its patented oil extraction process to Great Canadian Oil Sands Limited (GCOS) for 150,000 GCOS shares, current value of which is about $1.5 million. Great Canadian Oil Sands became the first modern oil producer in the Athabasca sands in 1967 when its 45,000-barrel-a-day, $260-million plant went on stream for the first time. (Production was later raised to 60,000 barrels a day.) The Sun Oil Company of Philadelphia owns 97 per cent of the shares of the company.

The leases and extraction pilot plant originally owned by Oil Sands and later taken over by the Alberta government were eventually to wind up in the hands of Can-Amera Export Refining Company Limited, ultimately under the control of Shaheen Natural Resources Limited of New York. (President John Shaheen is well known to Canadians as a friend of former Newfoundland premier Joey Smallwood and builder of the controversial oil refinery at Come-By-Chance, Newfoundland.) A second, $1.6-billion plant being constructed by the Syncrude consortium of multinational oil companies (Atlantic Richfield, Imperial, Cities Service and Gulf) is scheduled to begin production in 1977, twenty-four years after Fitzsimmons wrote his report on his own experiences in the tar sands.

Lest it be thought that International Bitumen was the only company to experience setbacks in its pioneering attempts to bring the Athabasca tar sands into commercial production, it is worth adding a postscript concerning Abasand Oils Limited. This company was organized by American oil magnate Max W. Ball in 1930, and ten years later, in 1940, Abasand had constructed a pilot hot-water extraction plant similar to Fitzsimmons', which was capable of processing 700 tons of tar sands a day. In less than a year's operation in 1941, the Abasand plant produced 17,000 barrels of bitumen which was refined into gasoline, diesel fuel and fuel oil. But in that same year the plant was destroyed by fire. Pressed by wartime shortages of oil, the federal government took over the Abasand property in 1943 and redesigned and reconstructed the facility. Before the new plant could be put into full operation it, too, was destroyed by a fire. The plant fire brigade stood by helplessly because newly installed water pumps had been improperly serviced and would not function.

On March 13, 1944, the Alberta legislature unsuccessfully petitioned the federal government to establish a royal commission inquiry into the happenings at the Abasand plant. Charging criminal sabotage, incompetence and mismanagement of public funds, the resolution stated: "Shortly after the Dominion government took control of the property, strange things began to happen. Out of the north came an endless string of weird incredulous [sic] stories of criminal incompetence, of scandalous waste of public funds and charges of sabotage were heard on every hand. So persistent were these ugly rumours that we decided to investigate and we found there was ample justification for the rumours." Following the second fire, the Abasand plant was abandoned.

Whatever one may think of Fitzsimmons' charges of a deliberate conspiracy to keep the oil sands out of production for the past thirty years, there is no denying that now the area has been opened up in earnest, what happens next will be of great importance to the development of Alberta and the rest of Canada. Not only are the potential social and economic ramifications of development of this huge resource enormous, but the environmental consequences for the 30,000-square-mile region likely to be affected (an area larger than the province of New Brunswick) will be profound.

The Athabasca tar sand deposits cover an area of five and three-quarter million acres, lying under an overburden of muskeg, glacial deposits and sediment that varies in depth from zero to 2,000 feet. With present technology, 150 feet is reckoned to be the maximum depth to which overburden can be removed by strip mining to expose the oil-soaked sands. Only about half a million acres of the deposit fall into this category, but these acres alone are estimated to contain about 74 billion barrels of crude bitumen. However, not all of this is considered to be recoverable. The Alberta Energy Conservation Board lists as "proved recoverable" only those deposits which underlie less than 150 feet of overburden and are at least as deep as the overburden to be removed and which contain 5 per cent or more crude bitumen by weight. Assuming that mining methods recover 90 per cent of the usable reserve, the board estimates that 38 billion barrels of crude bitumen are "proved recoverable" from the Athabasca deposits. The GCOS plant currently operates at a crude bitumen to synthetic crude oil conversion rate of about 70 per cent, while the proposed Syncrude plant expects to be able to turn as much as 75 per cent of the bitumen it produces into crude oil. Using the more conservative 70 per cent figure, the 38-billion-barrel proved reserve would yield 26.5 billion barrels of synthetic crude oil. At the 1974 Edmonton price of about $4 a barrel for synthetic tar sands crude oil, this proved deposit is worth $86 billion. At a more likely price in the future of $10 a barrel, it is worth $260 billion. That's $13,000 for every man, woman and child in the country.

The additional 552 billion barrels of bitumen trapped in Athabasca sands which are covered by between 150 and 2,000 feet of overburden are not included by the Alberta energy agency in its estimates of recoverable oil in the province because no practical

TABLE 3   THE ALBERTA TAR SANDS

Deposit	Overburden depth (feet)	Area (millions of acres)	Crude bitumen in place	Recoverable crude bitumen
			(billions of barrels)	
Athabasca	0-150	490	74	38
	150-2000	5260	552	—
Cold Lake	1000-2000	3160	165	—
Peace River	1000-2000	1180	50	—
Wabasca	250-1000	764	30	—
	1000-2500	1000	23	—

SOURCE: Alberta Energy Resources Conservation Board.

method of in situ recovery has yet been demonstrated. For this same reason, none of the deposits in the Cold Lake, Wabasca or Peace River tar sand regions are listed as recoverable either, although the three areas are thought to hold over 100 billion barrels of crude bitumen in total.

The basic problem of in situ recovery is reducing the viscosity of the bitumen to the point where it can be pumped to the surface. Over the years, many methods have been tested in the Athabasca region, including the pumping of kerosene-like diluents into the sands and high-pressure hot water or steam injection. The thinned or emulsified bitumen may be recovered through the same well into which the steam, hot water or diluent is pumped, or it may be pumped to the surface through other wells drilled nearby. In 1959 one American company proposed an experiment in which a nuclear bomb would be exploded underground to heat the bitumen. Tentative approval for the test was forthcoming from the Alberta government, but Ottawa vetoed the plan, citing potential adverse effects on nuclear test ban treaty negotiations. In view of Canada's strenuous objections to underground nuclear tests recently carried out by the United States in Alaska, it is doubtful that the project will ever be revived. At present, Amoco (Canada) Petroleum Company, Imperial Oil and Shell Canada are all operating major experimental in situ recovery projects in Alberta. Although the results of their tests are closely guarded corporate secrets, the Alberta Energy Conservation Board has declared itself to be optimistic that a commercial in situ process will have been developed within ten years.

Any foreseeable in situ recovery operation is likely to be very much less efficient than current strip-mining and hot-water recovery methods, but even if only 20 per cent of the bitumen is recovered from sands buried beneath more than 150 feet of over-burden, as much as 110 billion barrels of crude bitumen yielding 80 billion barrels of synthetic crude could be recovered. This would boost total synthetic crude production from the Athabasca deposit to 106.5 billion barrels.

The significance of the Athabasca reserves is seen in the following comparison with conventional reserves remaining in other parts of the world:

Region	Remaining reserves (billions of barrels)
North America	57.4
Caribbean and South America	32.6
Western Europe	12.0
Middle East	360.0
Far East, Australasia	15.5
Africa	105.0
Soviet Bloc and China	100.0
Total	682.5

In a purely Canadian context, it can be noted that the 26.5 billion barrels of synthetic crude classed "proved recoverable" from the Athabasca sands is enough oil to theoretically fill the country's entire petroleum demands for the next twenty-five years, assuming a yearly rate of growth in demand of 5 per cent. Development of a successful in situ extraction process would, of course, greatly extend this period.

The question being asked in the wake of the sobering petroleum shortages that began appearing in 1973 is: how soon will the Athabasca sands be producing truly significant quantities of oil? As of the end of 1973, only about 7 million barrels of synthetic crude had been taken out of the Athabasca region. But the GCOS plant is continuously adding to this total with its daily output of 60,000 barrels, and the $1.6 billion Syncrude facility now under construction and scheduled to begin production in 1977 will be adding another 105,000 barrels a day by 1980 and 125,000 barrels a day by 1984. By early 1974 three other groups had applied to the Alberta government for permission to construct extraction and refining plants in the Athabasca region: Shell Oil wants to build a 100,000-barrel-a-day plant by 1980; Petrofina Canada Limited, Hudson's Bay Oil and Gas, Murphy Oil and Candel Oil have grouped together under the name Athabasca Oil Sands Project to propose construction of a 122,000-barrel-a-day plant which would begin production in 1982; and Home Oil Limited, the only Canadian-owned company in the Athabasca sweepstakes, has applied for permission to build a 100,000-barrel-a-day plant which would be completed sometime "in the early 1980s." Each of these new plants would likely cost in excess of $1.3 billion.

The obvious starting point in trying to decide on the optimum rate of production for the Athabasca tar sands is a look at the projected future supply and demand for oil in Canada. The graph in Figure 1 has been adapted from the federal Department of Energy, Mines and Resources estimates. Because the price of oil influences the amount that can be produced (a higher price means less-accessible sources can be tapped), the graph has been based on a set price of $6 a barrel. This is considered to be the lowest price at which most inaccessible reserves could be exploited, so that a higher price would tend to increase supplies, but only by a relatively small amount. On the other hand, markedly higher prices would likely decrease demand significantly—perhaps, in the long run, by as much as 25 per cent. Three further qualifications

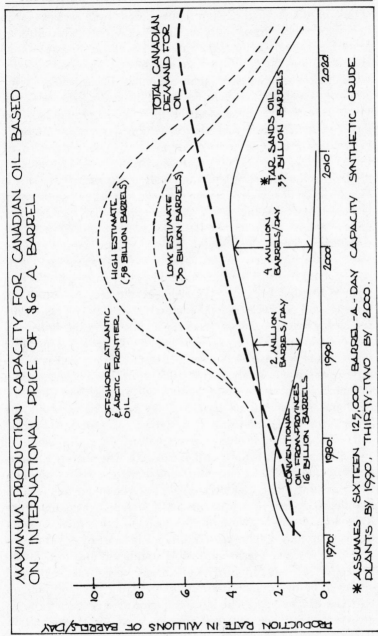

MAXIMUM PRODUCTION CAPACITY FOR CANADIAN OIL BASED ON INTERNATIONAL PRICE OF $6 A BARREL

TOTAL CANADIAN DEMAND FOR OIL

OFFSHORE ATLANTIC & ARCTIC FRONTIER OIL

HIGH ESTIMATE (58 BILLION BARRELS)

LOW ESTIMATE (30 BILLION BARRELS)

*TAR SANDS OIL 35 BILLION BARRELS

4 MILLION BARRELS/DAY

2 MILLION BARRELS/DAY

CONVENTIONAL OIL FROM PROVINCES 16 BILLION BARRELS

PRODUCTION RATE IN MILLIONS OF BARRELS/DAY

1970   1980   1990   2000   2010   2020

* ASSUMES SIXTEEN 125,000 BARREL-A-DAY CAPACITY SYNTHETIC CRUDE PLANTS BY 1990, THIRTY-TWO BY 2000.

FIGURE 1

should be stated: since no significant oil finds have yet been made in either the Atlantic offshore region or in the Arctic (certainly no finds big enough to justify construction of pipelines or other transportation facilities), the curves showing projected supplies from these sources are highly speculative. Secondly, some authorities would argue that the 16-billion-gallon figure assigned to ultimate reserves of crude from the western provinces is too large, in view of the fact that after thirty years of intensive exploration proved reserves in 1974 stood at only about seven billion barrels. Thirdly, the estimate of recoverable tar sands oil used (35 billion barrels) is undoubtedly too conservative, if it is assumed that in situ recovery methods will be developed by 1985. However, since it is the *rate* of tar sands production that concerns us here and a maximum rate has been assumed, the chart can be considered accurate, despite its conservatism, at least until the tar sands production curve begins to decline after the year 2000.

It is clear from this graph that despite declining production from exhausted conventional wells in the western provinces Canada's oil reserves could theoretically provide complete self-sufficiency for the Canadian market well into the next century and still provide for a healthy level of exports. In 1990, for instance, the excess of supply over domestic demand—the amount available for export—would be about two million barrels a day, even under the more conservative estimate of Arctic and offshore supplies. By 2000 another million barrels a day would be available for export. It is a very comforting long-term picture for both Canada and its export markets in the United States.

Unfortunately, it is not a realistic picture. The main problem is not with the projected outlook for offshore and Arctic supplies, which assumes, first, that large oilfields will be found, and second, that the equivalent of at least one 48-inch oil pipeline will be built by 1980 and one or two more by 2000, to bring total carrying capacity up to 3 million barrels a day. This sort of development projection does not seem impossibly optimistic. But look at the projected tar sands supply. The graph assumes tar sands crude oil output to be two million barrels a day by 1990 and four million barrels a day by 2000. The limiting factor here is neither known recoverable bitumen reserves nor the need for transportation facilities, which need only extend to existing pipelines at

Edmonton and can easily and quickly be built. The problem is that in order to boost tar sands production to two million barrels a day by 1990, a total of sixteen Syncrude-sized, 125,000-barrel-a-day, $1.3-billion plants would have to be built in the Athabasca sands. That's one plant a year between 1974 and 1990. To achieve a tar sands crude oil output of four million barrels a day by 2000, an additional sixteen plants would have to be built between 1990 and 2000—one new plant every seven and a half months.

While these goals for tar sands output may not be impossible in a Herman Kahn world of draconian economic measures and indentured labour, they are clearly undesirable. The most authoritative report on Athabasca tar sands development was made by an interdepartmental committee of more than fifty Alberta provincial civil servants in 1972. It predicted "complete chaos" if a construction rate of even one plant a year were attempted. Immense royalty payments and vastly greater inflows of construction capital would disrupt not only the Alberta economy but the entire Canadian economy, particularly since Athabasca development would be taking place alongside such immensely costly projects as Arctic gas and oil pipelines. The resulting inflation would be pushed out of all reasonable bounds by intense and unavoidable labour shortages. The population of Alberta would grow so rapidly that it is inconceivable that growth in the infrastructure of social services, housing and the like could keep pace. "Complete chaos" does not seem to be an overstatement of the probable state of affairs.

The Alberta civil service report went on to recommend a development rate of one Syncrude-sized plant (125,000-barrels-a-day output) every four years, for a total output by 2000 of one million barrels of synthetic crude a day. And in fact, it seems likely that shortages of labour and materials will limit construction to such a rate whether planners accept it or not. The Syncrude consortium, which hopes to have its plant in operation by 1977, reportedly found it necessary early in 1974 to ask Shell Oil to delay construction on the latter's Athabasca plant so that existing labour and material shortages would not be further exacerbated. Shell had planned to have its plant in operation in 1980, three years after Syncrude's start-up.

If we re-draw the supply/demand graph in Figure 2, leaving the assumptions about production from the western provinces, the Arctic and offshore reserves untouched, but adopting the four-plant-a-year forecast for tar sands development, a more realistic picture of probable future supply/demand conditions emerges.

Although neither graph is intended to present anything more than a very rough projection of future conditions in the Canadian oil market, some obvious conclusions can be drawn from a comparison of the two. The first is that future oil exports can be justified under a policy of Canadian self-sufficiency in oil only if the tar sands are opened up at an excessive rate. (Figure 3 speaks eloquently of current export policy.) This is certainly true if the low estimate of Arctic and offshore oil reserves turns out to be the accurate one; but even if the high estimate is accepted, it is clear that the area on Figure 2 bounded by the demand curve on the bottom and the dome of the "high estimate" curve above, which represents Canada's total excess supply, is too small to justify exports. To export this oil because it represents a short-term excess of supply over domestic demand would be irresponsible: a wiser policy would insist that it be kept out of production until it is needed in Canada, around the year 1995, according to the projections in Figure 2. By so doing, Canadians could hope to extend the period of the country's self-sufficiency in oil by a significant length of time—perhaps a decade or more.

As a corollary, it becomes clear why Herman Kahn and anyone else whose first loyalty is to the United States would want to see the oil sands developed as rapidly as possible; only if the sands are developed at a rate comparable to that projected in Figure 2 can continued oil exports from Canada to the United States be justified. Only then can Canada hope to meet her own domestic demand and still produce ample short-term surpluses for export. The costs to Canada would, as has already been observed, be enormous, but that is a consideration of only secondary importance to an energy-starved United States. Which is all the more reason for it to be a matter of primary importance to Canada in its attempts to decide on the best way to go about developing the tar sands.

If the social and economic costs of development of the Athabasca tar sands are likely to be high, the environmental costs

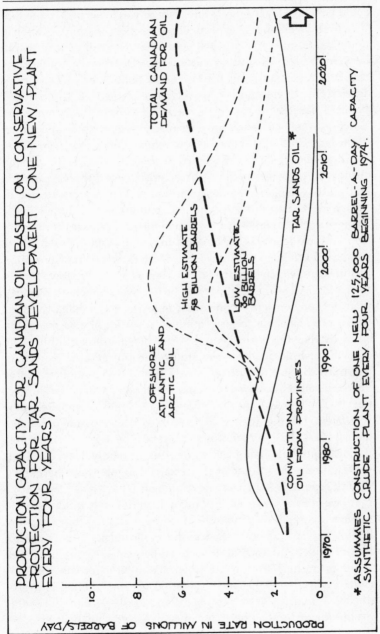

PRODUCTION CAPACITY FOR CANADIAN OIL BASED ON CONSERVATIVE PROJECTION FOR TAR SANDS DEVELOPMENT (ONE NEW PLANT EVERY FOUR YEARS)

TOTAL CANADIAN DEMAND FOR OIL

OFFSHORE ATLANTIC AND ARCTIC OIL

HIGH ESTIMATE 58 BILLION BARRELS

LOW ESTIMATE 26 BILLION BARRELS

CONVENTIONAL OIL FROM PROVINCES

TAR SANDS OIL *

PRODUCTION RATE IN MILLIONS OF BARRELS/DAY

1970   1980   1990   2000   2010   2020

0   2   4   6   8   10

* ASSUMMES CONSTRUCTION OF ONE NEW 125,000 BARREL-A-DAY CAPACITY SYNTHETIC CRUDE PLANT EVERY FOUR YEARS BEGINNING 1974.

FIGURE 2

could be truly staggering. While little research has been done into the environmental effects of in situ extraction, the impact of strip mining and hot-water processing is relatively well defined. It can be summarized this way: partial or total removal of surface vegetation; partially disrupted to totally obliterated surface drainage (creeks, rivers and lakes); extensive changes to groundwater patterns caused by vastly increased soil permeability once the water-resistant tar sands have been removed; altered topography of the land caused by mine pits and mine tailing deposits; massive withdrawals of surface water from streams and rivers causing changes to their rate-of-flow characteristics (and thereby altering entire ecosystems in the area); heated effluent water causing all the changes attributed to thermal pollution; and atmospheric changes such as winter ice fogs and emission of gases containing sulphur dioxide and other noxious compounds. In addition, there will be environmental changes caused by extensive transportation facilities and expansion of Fort McMurray and other townsites in the region. All of these effects will be felt over a much greater area than the 500,000 acres (780 square miles) of the Athabasca sands which are amenable to strip mining. What all of this means, in effect, is that the entire hydrosphere, biosphere and lithosphere (and to some degree even the atmosphere) of an area more than one-third the size of Prince Edward Island will be obliterated or very substantially altered. A vastly greater area will suffer indirect effects. The task will then be to design and build a completely new ecosystem for the region so that it will once again become a viable, life-sustaining environment. It will be a job of enormous, if not impossible, complexity, one we normally leave to God.

Despite the magnitude of the reclamation job, the Alberta civil service report on Athabasca development reported as late as 1972 that "we are not aware of any [my italics] research with respect to tailings disposal, reclamation or revegetation." This shocking finding applied to both industry and government. A more precise idea of the environmental impact can be gained by taking a look at the operations of a tar sands extraction industry consisting of eight Syncrude-sized plants supported by strip mining and producing a million barrels of synthetic crude a day. It is this magnitude of production that can be expected shortly after 2000, if the one-plant-every-four-years guideline is followed.

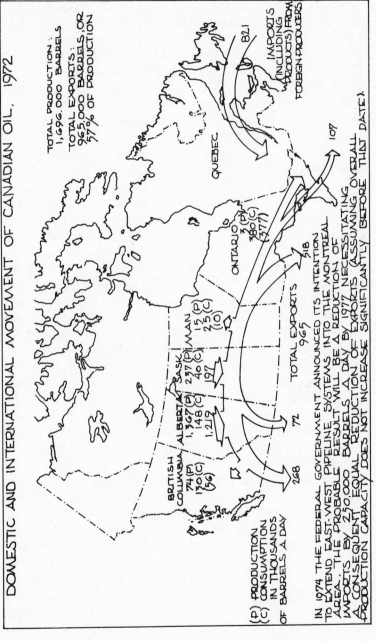

DOMESTIC AND INTERNATIONAL MOVEMENT OF CANADIAN OIL, 1972

TOTAL PRODUCTION :
1,696,000 BARRELS

TOTAL EXPORTS:
965,000 BARRELS, OR
57% OF PRODUCTION

IMPORTS (INCLUDING PRODUCTS) FROM FOREIGN PRODUCERS

821

QUEBEC

ONTARIO
3 (P)
380 (C)
(377)

107

BRITISH COLUMBIA
74 (P)
130 (C)
(56)

ALBERTA
1,367 (P)
148 (C)
1,219

SASK.
237 (P)
40 (C)
197

MAN.
15 (P)
25 (C)
(10)

TOTAL EXPORTS
965

518

72

268

(P) PRODUCTION
(C) CONSUMPTION
IN THOUSANDS
OF BARRELS A DAY

IN 1974 THE FEDERAL GOVERNMENT ANNOUNCED ITS INTENTION
TO EXTEND EAST-WEST PIPELINE SYSTEMS INTO THE MONTREAL
AREA. THE PROBABLE RESULT WILL BE A REDUCTION OF
IMPORTS BY 250,000 BARRELS A DAY BY 1977 NECESSITATING
A CONSEQUENT EQUAL REDUCTION OF EXPORTS (ASSUMING OVERALL
PRODUCTION CAPACITY DOES NOT INCREASE SIGNIFICANTLY BEFORE THAT DATE).

FIGURE 3

Surface mining to support such an industry would involve 2,200 acres a year, or about six acres a day. Since an average of three to five tons of material must be moved, processed and disposed of for each barrel of oil produced, a total of 375,000 to 625,000 tons of earth and sand will be dug up each day to support each plant. That's between three million and five million tons a day for all eight plants—a total of 1.2 billion to 1.8 billion tons of earth and sand a year physically moved, stored and processed. As much as 20,000 acres could be denuded and disrupted at any one time before a balance is established between disturbed and reclaimed land.

Part of the approximately 700 million tons of overburden removed each year will be dumped into previously excavated mine pits along with the cleaned sands, and much of the rest will be used for construction of huge dykes to hold the 42 million cubic feet a day or 15.3 billion cubic feet a year of liquid tailings from hot-water processing containing large quantities of oil (5 per cent of total bitumen processed), phenols, chlorides, nitrates, sulphates, iron and suspended silt. Because it is so highly contaminated, only a portion of this water can be sufficiently clarified by settling in the tailing ponds to be recycled through the hot-water extraction plant. The rest must eventually be pumped into mined-out pits or stored behind dykes as high as three hundred feet until some practical method of decontamination and clarifying can be found. Virtually nothing is known about the rate of seepage from these ponds or their effects on ground water. Existing ponds have been built on the banks of the Athabasca River: the effect on downstream ecology of a breach in a dyke and the release of millions of gallons of oily, chemical-laden water would be catastrophic. Even if the tailings are successfully contained they will have an effect on wildlife, since the Athabasca sands are on a major North American waterfowl flyway and birds landing on the ponds could not be expected to survive the combined effects of heat (the water is discharged to the ponds at 130 degrees Fahrenheit), oil and chemicals. A successful system of keeping migrating waterfowl from landing on these vast areas of open water is difficult to envisage.

Once the bitumen has been separated from the sand in the hot water extraction plant, it must be further treated to convert it to commercially acceptable crude oil. The first step in this process involves thermal cracking of the bitumen molecules, which produces a residue of carbon in the form of petroleum coke. This coke, which contains 6 per cent sulphur by weight, is burned to provide heat for the various extraction and refining processes in the plant. It is currently proposed that all of this sulphur be allowed to escape into the atmosphere along with the rest of the combustion gases from the coke burned as fuel. The sulphur equivalent of these SO_2 emissions from our eight plants would be about 2,100 tons a day, or 766,000 tons a year. By comparison, total SO_2 releases to the atmosphere from all thermal power generating stations in Canada in 1971 were only about 500,000 tons. This volume of air pollution being produced in such a compact area would be a serious problem under the best conditions, but one environmental study of the Athabasca region registered temperature inversions (weather conditions which hold pollutants close to ground level rather than allowing them to rise and disperse) on 82 per cent of winter days. The disastrous effects of heavy SO_2 pollution on vegetation can be previewed in the moon-like landscape surrounding the Sudbury, Ontario, nickel-smelting industry, a region that seems destined to lose its title of air pollution capital of Canada to the tar sands area.

It should be noted, as a saddening postscript, that the downstream area of the Athabasca River system (the area most likely to suffer environmental damage from tar sands exploitation) is, according to the federal Department of Energy, Mines and Resources, the biologically richest part of northwestern Canada, and is the region where there are perhaps more Indians making a living directly from the land than anywhere else in the country.

Given the magnitude of the environmental problems associated with strip mining and processing of the Athabasca tar sands, it is simply inconceivable that large-scale development can take place without catastrophic effects on a very large portion of the northwestern Alberta environment. The best that can be hoped is that development will take place at a responsible rate—perhaps one plant each four years as recommended by the Alberta civil service study—and that every effort will be made to keep the environmental impact to the lowest level possible. Unfortunately, even these modest hopes seem to have little support currently; the

Alberta government in 1974 was talking about a rate of development of one new plant every two years (twice the rate recommended by its own civil servants), and little real concern is being shown for the urgent need for vast increases in environmental and reclamation research. On March 7, 1972, G. W. Govier of the Alberta Energy Resources Conservation Board (which regulates development of the tar sands) made a speech to the American Petroleum Institute in Houston, Texas, in which he listed the problems facing increased tar sands exploitation as: failure to develop a commercial in situ process (although, he said, experimental work was promising); high and continually increasing capital costs; and high skilled labour requirements. Offsetting these problems, he told the American oil men, were the following advantages: the synthetic crude is of premium quality; the resource is of enormous size and virtually fully proven; no serious transportation problems exist; the supply is secure and in a stable political environment; the Alberta government has a "progressive attitude toward further development"; and *"no serious environmental problems exist"* (my italics). Such a statement leaves one breathless.*

4.
Nuclear Promises

It has often been argued that the post-World War Two decision to develop nuclear energy as the prime alternative to energy produced from fossil fuel combustion was not a rational one based on any reasoned appraisal of costs and benefits, but came rather as an emotional reaction to the horror of Hiroshima and Nagasaki.

* See Appendix 2.

The taming and domestication of the monster atom would some-how ease the Allies' collective guilt for the unspeakable carnage that finally brought Japan to her knees in 1945. No balanced analysis of the options available in the search for cheaper energy could have resulted in the choice of nuclear fission, with all its attendant problems of radioactive waste disposal and risks of cancer-inducing radiation leakages. Or so the argument goes.

While this rationale undoubtedly contains an element of the truth—perhaps the one most likely to withstand analysis from the perspective of historians of the distant future—the bare facts of the case point to a more mundane reason for the decision to develop and promote nuclear power. Thanks to the intensive and successful wartime drive to build an atomic bomb, research into nuclear power was given an insurmountable head start over investigations into any of its competitors. It would simply not have made "economic sense" to shelve the immense capital investment made in developing nuclear reactors for production of plutonium for bombs without seeking to exploit the commercial potential of atomic power.

Military decisions also played a key role in determining the particular breed of nuclear reactor chosen by the world's first two reactor-operating nations, Canada and the United States. By the end of World War Two, Canada found herself the possessor of a large pool of nuclear expertise and two almost-complete heavy water reactors, thanks to a wartime decision to shift the world's most advanced reactor research program from Luftwaffe-threatened Cambridge to Montreal and eventually to top-secret facilities at Chalk River. When the fighting ended in Europe and the British scientific team returned home, Canada retained a competence in heavy-water reactor design second to no other nation in the world. Fortunately, the heavy water concept fitted Canada's industrial abilities and resource availability ideally; if this had not been the case, it is doubtful whether the nation would have been capable of supporting a start-from-scratch program to design and build some other type of reactor. The American reactor, which differs from Canada's in several important respects, grew out of the design for the reactor used in the U.S. Navy's atomic submarine fleet, and it made use of facilities that were required anyway for fabrication of nuclear bombs. It seemed the obvious choice at the time but, in retrospect, the advantages of that particular design are less than compelling. Britain's post-war reactor program explored a number of novel pathways in design, most of which have recently been turning into blind alleys. The result has been that the nation which gave wartime research into atomic energy its biggest initial boost is now shopping around in Canada and the United States for foreign-designed nuclear reactors to meet its pressing energy demands.

In the spring of 1974 the U.S. Atomic Energy Commission reported to Congress that during the previous year, nuclear generating capacity had tripled to about 65,000 megawatts and that the number of nuclear power plants in operation in the country had increased from 29 to 42. The share of total American electricity demand supplied by atomic reactors had increased from two per cent at the beginning of 1973 to 6 per cent at the end of the year. Eighty more nuclear power plants were under construction, and 64 others were in the advanced planning stage.

This is only the beginning: by 1980 nuclear power plants are expected to be supplying a third of U.S. electricity demand—a total of nearly 150,000 nuclear megawatts. The cost of the plants alone will be in the order of $45 billion, with a comparable sum being required for nuclear fuel. By the year 2000, it is expected that 750,000 megawatts of a total electricity demand of 1,650,000 megawatts will be supplied by nuclear plants. (The projected total world nuclear power output for the year 2000 is set at about 4 million megawatts.)

The Canadian nuclear program is, naturally, more modest, but it is expected to grow just as quickly. By 1974 the four 514-megawatt reactor units at Pickering, Ontario, a 22-megawatt reactor at Rolphton and a 200-megawatt reactor at Douglas Point on Lake Huron were supplying 12 per cent of Ontario's electricity demand. With the 250-megawatt reactor at Gentilly, Quebec, on the St. Lawrence River, Canada's total nuclear power capacity added up to 2,528 megawatts of electricity. By 1985 new plants at Pickering, Darlington and Bruce in Ontario and at Gentilly in Quebec will have increased that total to about 14,000 megawatts, and projections for the year 2000 place output at more than 150,000 megawatts.

All of the nuclear power plants built or planned for construction in Canada are of the CANDU (Canada-deuterium-uranium) design, which uses heavy water as a moderator. In the United States virtually all the plants built or planned to date have used a "light" or ordinary water moderator, and are referred to as LWR (Light Water Reactor) reactors. The difference is significant, and a small detour into the world of reactor engineering is necessary to explain why.

The nuclear reactor in an electricity-generating plant is used as a source of heat for producing steam to drive turbines which, in turn, drive the generators. The heat is produced in the reactor when the uranium fuel is immersed in a moderator, which permits the well-known atomic chain reaction to take place. The moderator is simply a material which slows the neutrons being given off by the radioactive U235 in the fuel to a speed at which they can be captured by the nuclei of other U235 atoms. When this capture occurs, it results in the splitting or "fissioning" of the atom. There follows a release of energy in the form of heat and radioactivity and the ejection of two or three neutrons travelling at high speed. These neutrons are, in turn, slowed by the moderator so that they can split other atoms, allowing the chain reaction to continue.

A number of materials can be used as moderators, but cost and engineering considerations have limited the choice to graphite, ordinary or "light" water and heavy water. Of these, heavy water is by far the most efficient, in that it is very effective in slowing the neutrons, yet absorbs few of them itself, so that most are left to find U235 atoms to split. This permits a more complete "burning" of the uranium fuel. Unfortunately, heavy water is also, at $20 a pound, by far the most expensive of the three moderators. (Heavy water, or deuterium oxide, differs from ordinary water in that the two hydrogen atoms in the water molecule are replaced by two deuterium atoms. Hydrogen atoms consist of a proton and one orbiting electron; deuterium atoms have a proton and a neutron at the nucleus and one orbiting electron.)

Graphite is also a relatively weak absorber of neutrons, but large amounts of the material are needed to effectively slow the particles to capture speed. This means that graphite-moderated reactors tend to be large, and therefore, expensive to build.

The big advantage of ordinary water as a moderator is, of course, its low cost: the big disadvantage is that it is a hungry neutron-absorber, which means that low-cost natural uranium cannot be used as a fuel, as it can in heavy water or graphite-moderated reactors. Natural uranium is composed mainly of non-fissionable U238; only about one in 140 parts of natural uranium is in the form of fissionable U235. If ordinary water is to be used as a moderator, the uranium fuel must be "enriched" through a costly and complex chemical process which increases the ratio of U235 to U238. This enrichment procedure makes the fuel too expensive to "throw away" once it has served its useful life in the reactor, so it must be reprocessed to reclaim the valuable plutonium that is created during the fission process. The plutonium is either stockpiled for future sale, used in the fabrication of nuclear weapons, or used as fuel for other types of reactors.

In the American LWR reactor, the enriched uranium fuel (held in a lattice of thin fuel rods) and the light water moderator are contained within a strong steel "pressure vessel." Reactivity within this pressure vessel, and therefore the amount of heat produced, is governed by a number of control rods made of materials which are very effective neutron absorbers. As these control rods are lowered farther into the fuel lattice or "reactor core," they slow or "poison" the chain reaction by absorbing neutrons, until there are too few neutrons available for the reaction to continue and it stops completely. As long as the reactor is allowed to function, however, large amounts of heat are produced and transferred to the light water moderator surrounding the fuel. In some reactors, the water is kept liquid under high pressure, and in others it is allowed to boil. In a "pressurized water" LWR, the hot water is pumped from the pressure vessel through a series of tubes in a steam generator, and then back into the vessel. The steam produced by heat transfer in the steam generator is, of course, used to drive the turbines which drive the electricity generators. In a "boiling water" LWR, the moderator is allowed to boil within the pressure vessel, and the steam produced goes directly to the turbines. In this arrangement the turbines become slightly radioactive since there is no mechanism for isolating the radioactivity induced in the moderator from them. However, this activity dies out quickly following shutdown, permitting direct access for maintenance.

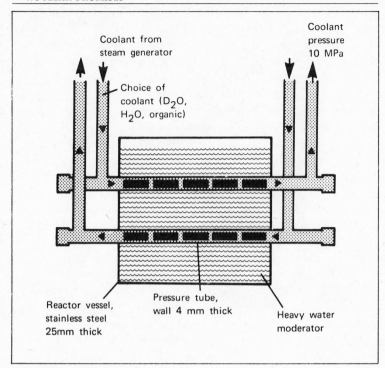

Coolant from
steam generator

Coolant
pressure
10 MPa

Choice of
coolant (D₂O,
H₂O, organic)

Reactor vessel,
stainless steel
25mm thick

Pressure tube,
wall 4 mm thick

Heavy water
moderator

Pressure tube reactor (CANDU)

The early designs for Canadian heavy water reactors also called for a pressure vessel to contain the fuel and moderator, but this idea was scrapped when more detailed engineering studies indicated that it would be very difficult (and probably beyond Canada's industrial capabilities) to produce the very large pressure vessels that would be needed in big generating stations. This meant that the moderator could not double as the reactor coolant (or heat transfer agent) as it does in the LWR reactor, since it could not be kept under pressure. So a reactor was designed in which the fuel is placed in a large number of long metal "pressure tubes" through which the coolant can be pumped at high pressure. The pressure tubes are held in place in a large cylindrical vessel called a calandria, which is filled with heavy water moderator. As in the LWR, provision is made for insertion of control rods to regulate the reactor by poisoning the chain reaction. As a further

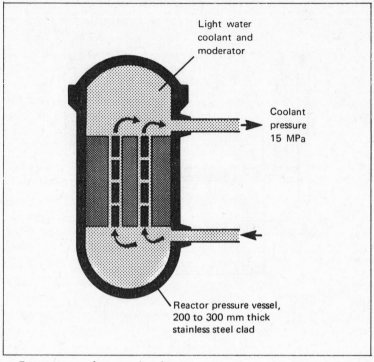

Light water
coolant and
moderator

Coolant
pressure
15 MPa

Reactor pressure vessel,
200 to 300 mm thick
stainless steel clad

Pressure vessel reactor (LWR)

precaution, a large dump tank is placed below the calandria, into which the moderator can be quickly drained to shut down the reactor. In most CANDU reactors, the coolant used is also heavy water; at Gentilly, however, the use of boiling light water is being tested. (Because boiling light water in the reactor pressure tubes reduces the efficiency of the reactor somewhat [since light water has a larger appetite for neutrons than heavy water] new designs for such reactors call for use of enriched fuel. This would clearly eliminate one of the CANDU reactor's main selling points—that it is capable of burning low-cost natural uranium fuel —but it would also mean that the plutonium contained in spent fuel from other CANDU reactors could be reclaimed and "burned" as the enrichment agent. This recycling of plutonium would significantly extend the life of known uranium reserves. But more of that later.)

The fact that the CANDU reactor does not operate under pressure within a pressure vessel, but instead uses pressure tubes, means that it can be refuelled while in operation. The fuel in each pressure tube is contained in a number of compact bundles of metal tubes; it is loaded in such a way that computer-controlled fuelling machines at either end of the calandria can load new bundles from one end of the pressure tube while spent bundles are simultaneously removed from the other. In the LWR, all of the fuel is replaced at the same time, and the reactor must be shut down about once a year for the change. This adds considerably to each LWR station's down-time, when no electricity can be produced or sold.

The initial capital costs of the LWR and CANDU reactors are about equal, and each is about twice the cost of a conventional fossil-fuelled generating plant. But because the natural uranium fuel used in the CANDU reactor is so cheap and relatively simple to fabricate, and because it need not be reprocessed; because on-power refuelling is possible; because there are fewer parts, fewer processes, less tubing, less pellet grinding and less hardware associated with a ton of CANDU fuel than with a ton of LWR fuel— because of all of these things, the total cost per unit of energy produced in a CANDU reactor tends to inflate only very slowly over the years as compared with either an LWR reactor or a fossil-fuelled plant. The chart below makes this clear:

PERCENTAGE OF TOTAL UNIT ENERGY COST

	CANDU 1972	CANDU 1987*	COAL 1972	COAL 1987*	LWR 1972	LWR 1987*
Capital	73	73	32	32	64	64
Operating and maintenance	12	25	5	10	9	19
Fuel	15	31	63	131	27	56
Total	100	129	100	173	100	139

* For an overall 5% inflation rate.

Clearly, the long-term costs of operating a CANDU power plant can be expected to be significantly lower than those of either a fossil-fuelled plant or an LWR plant.

Some additional light can be shed on the question of long-term cost by singling out the area of enrichment of materials. Both the

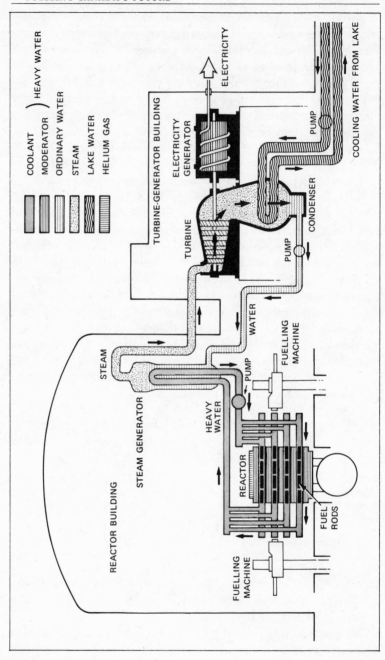

COOLANT
MODERATOR } HEAVY WATER
ORDINARY WATER
STEAM
LAKE WATER
HELIUM GAS

COOLING WATER FROM LAKE

ELECTRICITY

ELECTRICITY

PUMP

TURBINE-GENERATOR BUILDING

ELECTRICITY GENERATOR

TURBINE

CONDENSER

PUMP

WATER

STEAM

FUELLING MACHINE

PUMP

STEAM GENERATOR

HEAVY WATER

REACTOR BUILDING

REACTOR

FUELLING MACHINE

FUEL RODS

CANDU and the LWR reactors require the support of outside enrichment facilities at some time during their life. The CANDU reactor needs water which has been highly enriched in deuterium; that is, it needs heavy water. (Heavy water occurs in nature in the proportion of one part heavy water to 7,000 parts ordinary water. In fact, CANDU moderator is about 99.8 per cent pure heavy water.) The LWR reactor requires natural uranium fuel which has been slightly enriched in the fissionable U235. These external enrichment facilities are expensive to build and operate, and they must grow as the nuclear reactor program which they are designed to support grows. The heavy water enrichment process is not as complex or costly as the U235 enrichment procedure, partly because heavy water is not radioactive. Uranium enrichment plants require elaborate safeguards to protect workers and the public from radiation. And it is also important to note that the required heavy water enrichment capacity for any given power utility is proportional to the *rate of increase* in nuclear generating capacity, while the required uranium enrichment capacity is proportional to the *total* nuclear capacity. In other words, once a CANDU reactor has its supply of heavy water moderator, only relatively tiny additional amounts are required yearly to make up for leakages. So, in effect, heavy water enrichment capacity need only be large enough to supply moderator for each new plant. But an LWR plant needs a complete new supply of enriched fuel every year (or so) of its life, so that fuel enrichment capacity must be large enough to supply every nuclear plant in the system with a complete supply of fuel each year. So, in a growing system, fuel enrichment costs bound upward very quickly. Once again, a chart will demonstrate the significance of this fact. The figures below assume that a hypothetical power utility has an existing capacity of 15,000 megawatts, one-third of which is nuclear, and that output is expected to increase by 7 per cent a year, with 50 per cent of that new capacity to be nuclear.

The CANDU-PHW system (Canada Deuterium Uranium-Pressurized Heavy Water) is used in Douglas Point, Pickering and Bruce nuclear power stations. Heavy water moderator surrounds the pressure tubes containing the fuel elements. Heavy water under high pressure is also used to transfer the heat from the fuel to ordinary water in the steam generator. This turns the ordinary water to steam which is fed to the turbine.

MEGAWATTS REQUIRING ENRICHMENT SUPPORT WORK

Year	1st	11th	21st	31st
CANDU	525	1,050	2,100	4,200
LWR	5,000	14,000	32,000	68,000

Canada has had its problems in supplying heavy water for its reactors, principally because of disastrous design and construction errors at the Glace Bay, Nova Scotia, plant being built by Deuterium of Canada Limited, which ended with the plant being completely disassembled and redesigned from the ground up. It is now owned by the province of Nova Scotia, and Atomic Energy Canada Ltd. engineers are handling the rehabilitation work. Production is expected to begin, eight years behind schedule, in 1974 and by 1979 should have reached about 400 tons a year. By 1974 Canada's heavy water production—from plants at Port Hawkesbury and Glace Bay in Nova Scotia and Bruce in Ontario —is expected to meet the nation's demand for the first time. Prior to that time, the country imported a total of over 2,300 tons of heavy water from the United States, Sweden, the Soviet Union and Britain to meet its needs.

Paralleling work on conventional reactors over the years has been development in several countries of a reactor in which more fuel is produced than is burned—a so-called "breeder reactor." Such reactors have been built and operated experimentally in Britain, France, the Soviet Union and the United States and there is considerable enthusiasm for the breeder as the "reactor of the future." The reactors described thus far employ some form of moderator to slow neutrons to a speed where there is a high likelihood of their coming into contact with and splitting other atoms of fissile material. However, it is possible to sustain a chain reaction without the use of a moderator, provided the fuel used is highly enriched in fissile material such as $U235$ or plutonium or thorium. In such a chain reaction each atom, when split, gives off more than two neutrons: since only one is needed to sustain the chain reaction, the rest are available for absorption by some "fertile" breeding material such as $U238$ (which is the main constituent of natural uranium). As it absorbs these "excess" neutrons, the fertile $U238$ is gradually converted to plutonium, which is fissile and therefore burnable in a reactor. Because the number of neutrons produced per fission in such a reactor is greater than two, it is possible to produce more fissile material than is used up in the so-called "breeding" process. Thus, an expanding breeder reactor program should be able to keep itself supplied with fuel.

In the most common breeder reactor design, the core of highly enriched fuel is very compact (to reduce neutron losses) and is surrounded on all sides by a blanket of fertile u238, which absorbs the excess neutrons as they leak out of the core. Both the core and the blanket are cooled by liquid sodium, which is a more efficient heat transport agent than water. Such reactors are referred to as liquid metal fast breeder reactors (LMFBR). The "fast" refers to the speed at which the unmoderated neutrons are travelling in the core and not to the rate at which breeding takes place. It is thought that it will take from seven to twenty years for a typical breeder reactor to double its initial inventory of fissile fuel.

The major advantage of the breeder reactor is, of course, fuel economy. Whether this is a significant advantage or not is the subject of some controversy, and depends in large measure upon the nation concerned. In the United States fuel economy is seen to be important and a major breeder development program was further accelerated by President Nixon as part of his "energy self-sufficiency" program of 1974. Promoters of the breeder program have argued that unless several breeders are operating in that country by the mid 1980s, economic supplies of uranium to fuel conventional reactors will be in seriously short supply. In Canada there exists no such concern over future fuel supplies. Part of the reason for this lack of concern lies, naturally, in the fact that Canada's reactor program is much smaller than the American. But there is another reason. Because the Canadian reactor uses heavy water moderator, it burns its fuel much more efficiently than American reactors. A CANDU reactor gets between 25 and 50 per cent more electricity out of a pound of uranium than does an LWR reactor. And because neutron absorption is so low with heavy water moderator, relatively large amounts of plutonium are produced in the fertile u238 in CANDU fuel (although not nearly enough to replace the fissile u235 burned in the process). This plutonium (as much as 50 per cent more than is produced in the

LWR) can be reclaimed for use as fuel. Thus, even if Canada's nuclear program were as big as that of the United States the question of future fuel supplies would not be a pressing concern for many years. By 1981 plutonium in "spent" fuel from Canadian reactors will amount to more than 8,000 kilograms (worth about $30 a gram) and the plants will be producing an additional 2,000 kilograms a year. Recycling of this plutonium would cut Canada's uranium requirements in half, although the reclamation process itself would be expensive. However, because fuel costs are such a small part of the total cost of a megawatt of power produced by a CANDU reactor, it is doubtful whether there will be any direct economic incentive in the foreseeable future for Canada to get into the plutonium recycling business. Even if the cost of uranium were to increase five times, to $45 or $50 a pound, CANDU power station costs would only go up by about 30 per cent, and the cost of electricity to the consumer would go up considerably less than this, according to estimates from Atomic Energy Canada Limited (AECL), the crown corporation responsible for nuclear energy. Japanese engineers have estimated that 4.5 billion tons of uranium in the oceans could be recovered at less than $50 a pound; there is also ample low-grade uranium in the earth's crust to fuel the world's reactors for some decades to come. How long these supplies will last depends, of course, on the type of reactors they are burned in: unfortunately it is still too early to see who is winning in the high-pressure international competition between heavy water and LWR salesmen. Many in the Canadian nuclear industry claim to see a growing preference among less industrialized nations for CANDU and other heavy water designs, but this could well be wishful thinking.

There is another, darker side to nuclear energy without examination of which any discussion would be incomplete. That is the question of safety. A mature reactor of the size currently in widespread use contains many thousands of times more radioactive material than was released by the Hiroshima bomb. The problem of reactor safety is mainly one of how to keep this deadly material away from the public.

Nuclear reactors are designed in such a way as to eliminate the possibility of a significant release of radioactivity outside the reactor building in the event of an accident in any single system. For a significant release to be possible, there must be an accident in the reactor itself, plus simultaneous accidents in one or more of the safety systems. And the safety systems are designed to operate independently both of one another and of the normal reactor control devices in order to minimize the risk of an accident to the reactor causing damage to safety systems. So the odds against accidental releases of large amounts of radioactivity beyond the reactor building or "containment structure" are very small.

The worst possible single accident that can occur in the normal operation of any nuclear reactor is a sudden and complete loss of coolant caused by the rupture of one of the main coolant-carrying pipes. The chain of events that would follow such an accident is different in different reactor designs. In an LWR, the coolant is also the moderator, so if the coolant is lost the reactor automatically shuts down, unable to sustain a chain reaction in the absence of light water moderator. However, there is enough heat generated within the fuel by radioactive fission products (created by neutron bombardment of U238 while the reactor is operating), and by the U235 itself, to cause any water remaining within the pressure vessel to flash into steam. This greatly increases the pressure within the reactor and could cause a rupture of the pressure vessel. So LWR pressure vessels must be capable of withstanding pressures much greater than those experienced in normal operation. In fact, they are designed to contain the highest pressures that could result from such a loss of coolant: the American Atomic Energy Commission (AEC) officially regards a rupture of the pressure vessel of any reactor built within its jurisdiction and according to its standards as impossible. While the labelling of a conceivable accident as impossible is a dubious exercise, it is no doubt true that the odds of such a sudden, explosive rupture of the pressure vessel are very, very small. In any case, the reactor containment building is specifically designed to prevent any significant leakage of radioactivity to the outside even if the pressure vessel were to break, so there is a second line of defence against such an "impossible" accident.

In the CANDU reactor, a loss of coolant does not shut down the reactor, because the reactor core remains immersed in its calandria of heavy water. In the event of an accident the reactor must be shut down by dropping a number of emergency control rods into the core. These rods are made of material which has a high capacity for absorbing neutrons (such as boron or cadmium). Once they are in place, too few "free" neutrons remain for the chain reaction to continue. CANDU reactors are also equipped with an emergency dump tank into which the heavy water moderator can be quickly released should the emergency control rods fail to function. At Bruce and all subsequent CANDU reactors, a third means of shutting down the reactor will also be available, in the form of a liquid neutron-absorbing substance or "poison" which can be pumped into the calandria in the extremely unlikely event that the control rods should fail and the heavy water cannot be dumped.

As in the case of the LWR, however, there is enough heat generated by fission products in the fuel even after the reactor has shut down to cause what coolant remains in the pressure tubes to flash into steam, creating an increase in pressure that could conceivably cause a breach of the containment structure. Once again, more than one line of defence is employed. The concrete containment structure itself is built to withstand great pressures. And in multi-reactor plants like Pickering (four operating reactors with four more under construction), a huge concrete "vacuum building" is connected to the reactor buildings by large concrete ducts. Before pressure within the containment structure can build to dangerous levels, the ducts to the vacuum building are automatically opened and the pressure is released. As the steam rushes into the vacuum building, it is condensed by a cooling spray of water. Since it is not considered economic to build such vacuum containment structures in conjunction with single-unit reactors like the one at Gentilly, a different method of coping with steam pressure must be used. The one chosen by AECL engineers involves housing a large water reservoir at the top of the reactor building. As steam pressure builds after a loss-of-coolant accident, water from this reservoir douses the inside of the reactor building, condensing the steam and thereby reducing the pressure. Should this dousing system fail, or for some reason prove to be inadequate, a tall stack is provided for venting the containment building. Use of the stack, unlike use of the vacuum building, obviously involves a release of radiation to the atmosphere. AECL engineers admit that in a serious accident as much as three to five curies of radiation could be released in this way; however, the effect of such a release on the population, they say, would be so small as to be undetectable. Nonetheless, it is unlikely that such a pressure release system would ever be used in a reactor located near a large population centre.

Once the problem of containing high steam pressures has been solved, the next task to be dealt with in protecting a reactor from damage due to a loss of coolant is provision of an emergency core cooling system. These are designed differently for different types of reactors, but their purpose is the same: to provide enough emergency coolant (light water in LWR's; light or heavy water in CANDU's) to keep temperatures within the reactor down to safe levels while the main cooling system is repaired. The obvious question then becomes: "What if the emergency cooling system should also fail?" Several reactor accidents have occurred in the United States in which emergency systems have not operated quickly enough or effectively enough to control overheating in the core completely, and the result has been a partial melt-down of the reactor core. Such partial melt-downs are serious enough in themselves, and it has typically taken a year or more to repair the damage done. But no breach of containment is involved and thus no large releases of radioactivity were experienced. However, if the emergency cooling system should fail completely, the result would be a complete melt-down of the reactor core. Such an occurrence involves so many variables that it has proved virtually impossible to predict accurately what might happen, but scientists who have examined the prospect speculate that the following events might take place in the case of an LWR burning enriched fuel: increasing temperatures would cause the reactor core to disintegrate, dumping the fuel rods on the pressure vessel floor in a compact jumble. This would intensify the heat produced to a degree where it might be impossible to cool the fuel, even if the pressure vessel were completely flooded with water. The fuel would melt its way through the pressure vessel and drop to the floor of the containment structure, where it would melt its way through the concrete floor and on down several feet into the earth. Because of the low level of enrichment of LWR fuel, there is no possibility that a "critical mass" of fissile material could result, so an atomic explosion is not possible. But how radiation could be contained in such an accident, and how the mess could eventually be cleaned up are problems calculated to baffle the most resourceful engineer.

In a CANDU reactor, the odds of such a disastrous melt-down following a loss-of-coolant accident are even more remote than they are in the LWR reactor; in fact, AECL safety engineers argue that it is impossible for a complete melt-down to occur in a CANDU reactor. The first line of defence lies in the emergency cooling system which, like the American system, is designed to be fail-safe. But beyond this, the unique pressure-tube design of the CANDU reactor offers further safety provisions. First, the reactor core is immersed in thousands of gallons of cool heavy-water moderator which acts as a heat sink. In the virtually incredible event of a triple accident in which the main coolant was lost, the emergency coolant system failed to function and the emergency control rods failed to drop into place to shut down the reactor (and, in the new designs, if the liquid poison pumps failed, too), the moderator would have to be dumped to stop the chain reaction. It would therefore not be available to act as a heat sink. But a back-up system is provided even for this eventuality: a sprinkler system sprays heavy water from the roof of the calandria at all times and would serve to cool the reactor core enough to significantly delay the overheating process. Long enough, perhaps, for repairs to be made to one of the failed safety systems.

We are by now so far into the realm of the implausible that to try to predict further events is probably a meaningless exercise, but for what it is worth, here is what AECL engineers think might happen if the heat being generated by fission products in the fuel were not quenched. The reactor core would disintegrate, as in the case of the LWR, and the pressure tubes and fuel would fall to the floor of the calandria. If no action were taken to flood the calandria at this point, the jumble might melt its way through and fall to the floor of the reactor containment structure. But that, it is believed, is where the melting would stop, because the mass of melted fuel and metal would not be compact enough to generate enough heat to allow it to continue its travels. The reactor building itself could be flooded at this point to bring things under control and no breach of the containment would occur.

To gain a better perspective on the likelihood of an accident occurring, it is worth quoting some figures prepared by AECL safety engineers. The chances of a major break in a main coolant pipe are estimated at between one in a thousand and one in ten thousand per reactor year. In other words, such an event might take place in any single reactor somewhere between once in a thousand and once in ten thousand years of operation. The odds of a major coolant pipe break occurring simultaneously with a failure of any *one* of the safety systems described are thought to be at least a thousand times greater than this: that is, such a dual accident might occur somewhere between once in a million and once in ten million years of reactor operation.

Nonetheless, accidents have a way of happening in spite of the odds against them. The problem with nuclear reactors is that while the odds of an accident occurring in which there might be a risk to the public are extremely small, the amount of damage that could be caused by such an accident is proportionally great.

The reactor design presenting the greatest potential hazard is clearly the liquid metal fast breeder reactor (LMFBR), to which the United States is committed. Because the mean neutron speed is so great (100 to 1,000 times that of an LWR and 10,000 to 100,000 times that of a CANDU reactor), everything happens much more quickly in a breeder. Thus the allowable reaction time to any accident is reduced dramatically. Moreover, the fuel used is so highly enriched that were even a partial melt-down to occur within the reactor core, it is possible for the fuel to be compacted to the point where a critical mass would be achieved and an atomic explosion could result. Such an explosion would not have the force of one caused by detonation of an atomic warhead, but it could lead to further compacting of fuel and further low-yield explosions. There is considerable debate in the scientific community as to whether any man-made containment structure could resist such an explosion. A partial melt-down did, in fact, occur during operations of a prototype LMFBR near Detroit, Michigan (the Enrico Fermi reactor), in 1966. Fortunately, the reactor was brought under control before an explosion could take place, but for the nearly four weeks it took to analyse the damage there were fears that repair work might jar the damaged fuel into a critical mass. Some very serious debate took place as to whether the city of Detroit should be evacuated. In the end, the fuel was safely removed, but the projected cost of rehabilitating the reactor was so great that it has been shut down permanently. On the other hand, the LMFBR at Dounreay in Scotland has been feeding power to the British grid since 1959 without serious mishap.

How serious are the potential consequences of a major release of radioactivity from a nuclear power station? The American AEC's own notorious 1957 Brookhaven report postulated the complete destruction of the containment system of a small LWR reactor —the so-called "maximum credible accident"—and estimated that 3,400 deaths, 43,000 injuries and property damage of $7 billion would result. A similar study by the University of Michigan forecast as many as 133,000 deaths. Nuclear engineers would argue, with some justification, that the accidents foreseen in these reports are not "credible" at all. Such a massive rupture of the containment structure could not possibly occur in normal operation of today's conventional, non-breeder reactor. Only some outside force such as the act of a saboteur or an earthquake could cause such damage, and even these events would be unlikely to cause serious radiation releases. Tight security around nuclear plants can always be tightened further to prevent acts of sabotage, it is argued, and anyway reactor buildings are among the strongest ever built by man and would yield only to an extremely large terrorist bomb. Precautions are also taken against earthquakes: the large multi-unit plant at Pickering, Ontario, for instance, is capable of withstanding the worst earthquake that is likely to occur in any hundred-year period, according to AECL engineers. They do not know, however, how it would fare in the more serious earthquake capable of occurring once in a thousand years.

Even under normal operating conditions, when all reactor systems are performing as designed, nuclear power plants release small amounts of radioactivity to the outside environment. And during minor accidents or system malfunctions slightly larger amounts often escape. In all nuclear nations, strict regulations set limits on the amount of radiation reactors are permitted to release both in normal operations and as the result of most accidents. These regulations are derived from limits established by two autonymous international organizations: the International Commission on Radiological Protection (ICRP) and the United Nations Scientific Committee on the Effects of Atomic Radiation (UNSCEAR). In Canada they are administered by the federal Atomic Energy Control Board, an independent panel which oversees both design and construction of reactors and assesses releases during operation. A similar separation of responsibilities exists in Britain, but in the United States the AEC is responsible for both reactor safety and design and promotion of nuclear power plants, a situation in which many American critics see a direct conflict of interest.

Allowable radiation release limits vary little from country to country (with one major exception, which will be mentioned below). And they are established with reference to both an individual living at the limit of a 3,000-foot "exclusion zone" around the reactor building and the rest of the population in general. Radiation doses are measured in "rems," which are defined in terms of the amount of energy absorbed by a gram of tissue as the result of exposure to radiation. The "background" radiation from radioactivity occurring naturally in the earth and from the sun—radiation to which everyone is constantly exposed—amounts to about 100 millirem or .01 rem a year. In addition to this, an average North American receives another 80-odd millirem from fallout (4 millirem), diagnostic X-rays (72 millirem), occupational exposures, and so on, for a total of just over 180 millirem total annual exposure from all sources.

The allowable dose limits from nuclear reactors in Canada are in addition to this average annual exposure, and are as follows:

MAXIMUM PERMISSIBLE DOSE LIMITS FROM NUCLEAR REACTOR

	Normal operation	Single accident*	Dual accident*
Individual at exclusion zone	0.5 rem/year/ person	0.5 rem/person	25 rem/person
General population	5 rem/person, over 30 years, or .167 rem/ yr./person	10,000 man-rem for total pop'n. affected	1 million man-rem for total pop'n. affected
Reactor workers	0.5 rem/yr./ person	0.5 rem/person	0.5 rem/person

* Assumed maximum frequency of single accident: one per three reactor years; of dual accident: one per 3,000 reactor years.

Some further information will help in interpreting these figures. There are two potential effects from exposure to radiation: acute effects which are the immediate result of short-term exposure to high levels of radiation causing tissue damage, temporary or permanent illness, or death; and delayed effects, which include leukemia and other cancers, and deformities or other genetic defects in the progeny of exposed persons.

It is estimated that a person exposed to a single 400-rem dose of radiation has a 50/50 chance of dying as a result of the acute effects. The lowest dose which causes a measurable acute effect (that is, measurable with current technology) is about 25 rem; a single exposure of the body to this amount of radiation causes a noticeable reduction in the white blood corpuscle count, lowering the body's resistance to infection. Note that this is the limit set for the dose absorbed by the most exposed member of the public as a result of a dual accident such as a simultaneous loss of reactor coolant and failure of one of the reactor safety systems.

There is presumed to be no lower limit or "threshold dose" for delayed effects such as cancer, and even the tiniest amounts of radiation exposure increase the odds of cancer occurring in an individual to some degree. Normal background radiation (0.1 rem/yr.), for instance, is thought to be the cause of a significant number of the cancers and birth defects occurring in the population every year. According to Dr. John W. Golfman and Arthur R. Tamplin of the Lawrence Radiation Laboratory in Livermore, California, an accumulated dose of 100 rem of radiation will double the incidence of most cancers in a large population. Lung cancer may increase by as much as 250 per cent. Using these and other estimates prepared in an AEC research program, Golfman and Tamplin have gone on to suggest that exposure of the entire American population to the maximum dose limits for normal reactor operation listed above, over a thirty-year period, would result in 16,000 extra cases of cancer and leukemia each year. A more recent study by the U.S. National Academy of Sciences–National Research Council concluded that such exposure would result in "from roughly 3,000 to 15,000 cancer deaths annually." Taking the most pessimistic of these estimates and applying them to Canada's population, we could expect perhaps 1,600 extra cancer and leukemia deaths in this country.

A more conservative estimate comes from Dr. G. C. Butler of Canada's National Research Council, who suggests that exposure of those living at the exclusion zone to the full allowable dose limits would cause 100 extra deaths from leukemia and other somatic effects per million individuals and 13 additional cases of birth defects per million live births. For the rest of the population, the increase in cancer would result in 30 extra deaths per million population and there would be 26 extra cases of genetic defects per million births.

It bears repeating that these dose limits are the maximum allowable. In the United States, experience to date has been that nuclear power plants typically release about one per cent of the allowable limits. In Canada, releases have been considerably higher than this, although they tend to fall with each new plant built. AECL engineers say that the reactor at Douglas Point has been releasing as much as 10 per cent of the maximum allowable; leakages from Pickering have been held to 2 to 3 per cent of the limit. According to these same engineers, the releases could be even further reduced through application of known technology, were there any incentive to do so.

The American AEC has recently provided such incentive in that country by announcing its intention to lower its permissible release limits for normal operation of most kinds of reactors to one hundredth of those listed above. Canada's AECB is studying the American decision, but seems unlikely to take similar action— at least not in the immediate future. Part of the reason for this inertia can be found in the fact that there is little public concern about the effects of radiation from power plants in Canada: only two provinces currently have nuclear power reactors and only one more (British Columbia) is likely to have one by the end of the decade; but even in the nuclear provinces of Quebec and Ontario there has been little resistance to nuclear power development. Furthermore, what resistance there is, is allowed no effective forum, since in Canada, unlike in the United States, there is no legal provision for public hearings during the application process for construction of a nuclear power plant.

This absence of public input to nuclear development plans pokes a gaping hole in the rationale most commonly used to justify the increased risk of exposure to harmful radiation presented by nuclear power plants. Proponents of nuclear power are wont to argue that the small risks inherent in expansion of nuclear power are more than offset by the benefits of cheap electricity. But they fail to point out that the public that is bearing the risks is never asked for its opinion on what is, after all, a purely subjective decision. In the United States, where public hearings are mandatory, the alleged preponderance of benefits over costs has been called into serious question by a number of public groups, to the extent where one (admittedly biased) observer—Ralph Nader—has predicted that public pressure will prevent the building of any more nuclear power plants after 1980.

Even if routine radiation releases from the reactors themselves were the only risks at issue, the argument for giving those who are exposed to the risk some voice in deciding whether the benefits make it all worthwhile would be unassailable. But the risks go far beyond these routine releases, and beyond even the very small risks of disastrous reactor accidents releasing massive amounts of radiation.

First of all, there is the problem of thermal pollution from nuclear power plants which, for safety reasons, must operate at lower steam pressures than conventional thermal plants and as a result discharge as much as 50 per cent more heat to their steam-cycle cooling water. This water (unlike the reactor coolant, which operates on a closed cycle within the reactor) is taken from nearby lakes and rivers in huge quantities and after a single trip through the steam generating system is pumped back out, slightly warmer than it was. A 3,000 megawatt CANDU station uses about two million gallons of cooling water a minute.

Heating the water in a lake or river causes an increase in bio-logical activity, which may take the form of "blooms" of weeds and algae (already a problem in Lakes Erie and Ontario and many other bodies of water because of phosphate fertilization over the years), thus contributing to the well-known ageing or "eutrophi-cation" process and lowering available oxygen levels. The warmer water and lower oxygen levels can lead to an increase in numbers of low-oxygen-tolerant fish species, most of which are currently considered "undesirable" for human consumption, and a decrease in the firm-fleshed varieties sought after by fishermen. Lower oxygen levels also mean that the water is less capable of breaking down sewage and other wastes, a vital consideration in heavily polluted bodies of water like Lake Erie. It is sometimes argued that the heat-induced increase in biological production resulting from thermal pollution is counterbalanced by the fact that most of the organisms passing through the plant's steam cycle are killed in the process. However, recent evidence suggests that a far smaller percentage of these organisms than had been thought are, in fact, killed. In any case, those that are killed supply fertilizer to promote a compensating growth among those that are unaffected. Among those organisms which experience an increase in growth activity in the warmer water are some which cause disease in fish and other aquatic animals, and which may be completely dormant at normal water temperatures. According to Dean E. Arnold, a research limnologist with the University of Michigan Great Lakes Research Institute: "In general, we can conclude that no desirable effects of heat discharges are likely; that undesirable effects may be produced directly; and that even if this does not happen, undesirable processes already underway may be accelerated."

By 1980, as much as one-fifth of all runoff water in the United States will be being used for power station cooling and in some areas the percentage will be much higher. It is expected, for instance, that the entire flow of the Colorado River will be used in the cooling process by 1980: the water temperature in the river could eventually rise to about 85 degrees, five degrees hotter than the highest temperature tolerable to the salmon which use the river as a major spawning ground.

An Ontario Ministry of the Environment study on thermal pollution postulates a one-degree rise in inshore areas as a maximum "acceptable" increase in water temperatures, and calculates that, for Lake Ontario, such an increase could be affected along the Ontario shoreline (to a distance of five miles out) by operation of about 14,000 megawatts of nuclear generating capacity. It goes on to point out that Ontario Hydro plans to build as much as 24,000 megawatts of nuclear capacity on Lake Ontario by 1990.

Methods of cooling the warm water discharged from power plants are available in wide array—all the way from simple cooling ponds to huge radiators similar to those in water-cooled automobiles. The main disincentive to wider use is the cost involved, which is estimated to add about 5 per cent to the price of a typical nuclear power station. However, if protection of the natural environment is to continue to be one of society's goals, these increased costs will have to be accepted in future.

The second major "external" area of risk in the development of nuclear energy as a source of power lies in the production of plutonium and other radioactive by-products of the fission process. Once created, these materials cannot be destroyed, and are rendered harmless only by the natural process of radioactive decay. This decay process—in which the radioactive matter is transformed by the release of atomic particles into a relatively inert element such as lead (a sort of alchemy in reverse)—can be over within a few moments or it can take centuries or even millennia to complete. It is measured in terms of the radioactive material's "half-life," which is the time it takes for the material to give up half of its remaining radioactivity. A useful rule of thumb states that a material loses all but one-millionth of its radioactivity over twenty half-lives, and that by the end of this period it presents little hazard to humans if dispersed in air or water.

Plutonium (which does not exist in nature) is the most potentially dangerous of the by-products of fission, for four reasons: it is probably the most toxic material known to man, with quantities measured in hundredths of grams capable of inducing cancer if ingested; it is produced in relatively large quantities in reactors now, and will be produced in vastly greater quantities if and when breeder reactors gain widespread acceptance; it has a very long half-life of about 25,000 years, so that our rule of thumb would indicate that it must be kept from human contact for at least 500,000 years; and it is relatively easily made into atomic bombs.

Most countries operating nuclear reactors which burn expensive enriched uranium fuel either have built, or plan to build, fuel reprocessing plants which lower overall fuel costs by separating and reclaiming enriched uranium and plutonium left in "spent" reactor fuel. The reclamation process involves dissolving the fuel in an acid bath and then chemically (and imperfectly) separating the acid solution into three streams: one containing mostly uranium, one containing mostly plutonium and the third containing a hodge-podge of wastes in the form of various radioactive fission products. The uranium is re-manufactured into fuel for conventional reactors. The plutonium is either sold to the government concerned for use in the fabrication of nuclear weapons (a sale which provides a hidden subsidy for the nuclear power program of that country) or is stockpiled for anticipated sale to operators of breeder reactors (which use it as fuel).

The third stream—which contains the fission products as well as a small amount of plutonium that has escaped the separation process—is concentrated as much as is feasible and then pumped through heavily shielded pipes to double-walled, refrigerated, stainless steel storage tanks, where it must be kept until its radioactivity dies out to safe levels (perhaps several hundred thousand years) or until some better method of storing it is found. One such method being explored in the United States, Britain, France, Germany and elsewhere involves solidifying the wastes into glass blocks which are then placed for perpetual storage in abandoned salt mines. Salt mines have been chosen because salt occurs in geologically stable areas where the danger of earthquakes is minimal and because the presence of salt implies the absence of water which could carry radioactivity into contact with humans. The experiment has had its technical setbacks, but nonetheless remains the most promising method of radioactive waste "disposal" currently under investigation. In the United States alone, about two billion gallons of this highly radioactive, perpetually boiling acid solution will have accumulated by 1995. Its safe management will be a colossal undertaking. And one may well wonder what men living centuries or even millennia from now will think of a single generation which has created such a burden for its children down through the ages for the sake of satisfying ephemeral economic criteria of a prodigiously wasteful society. The assumption that future generations will find a way to permanently and safely dispose of our radioactive garbage is likely to be valid only if it is also assumed that future societies will choose to carry on down the path of innovation in technological hardware so recently embarked upon by our own great-grandfathers. That the wisdom of such a course is at least debatable should find little argument among anyone who has lived through the last twenty years of technological "progress."

Perhaps a more pressing concern for the current generation is that of adequately safeguarding plutonium from theft by terrorist blackmailers. That this is a very real concern has been acknowledged by the AEC, which has instituted a program of tightening security in plants where plutonium is produced and around buildings where it is stored. Though it is highly toxic if ingested, radioactivity in pure plutonium is low enough for it to be handled relatively safely. Many physicists have recently been trying to alert the public to the fact that virtually any bright, well-educated psychopath could build an atomic bomb small enough to be concealed in a car using only a small amount of stolen plutonium (or U235) and books and equipment readily purchaseable from scientific equipment retailers. The "trigger quantity" of U235 that would be required for such a crude, home-made bomb is somewhere between 5 and 20 kilograms—a grapefruit-sized mass; the trigger quantity for plutonium is something over 2 kilograms. In the last quarter of this century nuclear power companies in the United States will, if growth occurs as expected, produce 10 million kilograms of plutonium. At any given moment a sizable fraction of this amount will be in transit from reprocessing plants to warehouses and from warehouses to reactors and so on—available for hijacking. (If reactor designs such as the LMFBR which burns almost pure U235 are proceeded with, a comparable amount of U235 will also be available.) To put it another way, an LWR capable of supplying electricity for an average-sized American city produces each year enough plutonium to obliterate that city in an explosion. Already enough high-grade plutonium has vanished from the production pipeline to make many bombs; before reconnaissance photographs revealed the existence of a Chinese uranium enrichment plant it was believed that the first Chinese nuclear weapons test was carried out with the help of some of the U235 known to have gone missing in the United States. In 1970 officials in a city in Florida received a blackmail note which contained a threat to wipe out the city unless a million-dollar ransom was paid. A day later a second note arrived which included an accurate sketch of a hydrogen bomb. The threat turned out to be a hoax perpetrated by a bright fourteen-year-old delinquent, and in any case a hydrogen or fusion-type bomb is probably impossible to build without elaborate scientific facilities, unlike the relatively easy-to-make fission bomb discussed above. But the incident was enough to send a chill down the spine of more than one physicist familiar with weapons design. Given the course of human history to date, it would seem almost inevitable that some group or individual or even a renegade government will eventually fulfil the worst nightmares of these physicists and explode an atomic device fabricated with hijacked plutonium or U235. Even if such a bomb were to fizzle in a very low-yield explosion, the effects of the radiation released would be devastating.

In Canada neither the problem of safeguarding plutonium nor of storing large volumes of radioactive liquid wastes has come up, because CANDU natural uranium fuel is so cheap to fabricate that no plutonium "subsidy" is required to keep nuclear power costs in line with those of electricity from other sources. So there is no economic need to reclaim plutonium from spent fuel by putting the fuel through a complex and expensive reprocessing plant. One would expect that the powers within Canada's nuclear industry would be well satisfied with this state of affairs, freeing them as it does to concentrate on devising comparatively straightforward methods for storing solid CANDU fuel bundles somewhere where they can be retrieved by future scientists and engineers, who will presumably know what to do with them.

However, strong pressures are being exerted within AECL to get the country into the fuel reprocessing business and much time and money is being spent on researching methods of solidifying and storing the liquid wastes that would result. Beyond an acknowledgment of the simple dynamics of nuclear power research, which push irresistibly in the direction of more and more "efficient" reactors burning more and more highly enriched fuel (in which plutonium can be burned as the enrichment material), it is difficult to understand why AECL would pursue such a high-risk course. Certainly it would seem clear that in this case the potential costs greatly outweigh any benefits in the form of marginally cheaper electricity.

Ironically, part of the reason for AECL's interest in reprocessing spent fuel can be found in the search for a solution to the waste storage problem. Spent reactor fuel contains two broad categories of dangerous material: plutonium and small amounts of other matter with very long half-lives; and the fission products, mainly cesium 137 and strontium 90, with half-lives in the order of thirty years. It is reasoned that if reprocessing methods can be improved to the point where better than 99 per cent of the plutonium and other long-lived matter can be removed from the fission products, the length of time for which these fission products will have to be stored will be greatly shortened—to perhaps six or eight hundred years from the half a million years required for plutonium to decay to safe levels. The plutonium could then be recycled in nuclear reactors forever. Or else it could be shot into space in a rocket, or . . . who knows what future generations will come up with? Such is the rationale which could get Canada into the fuel reprocessing business within the next few years.

But for the moment the main thrust of AECL's waste storage work involves methods of containing entire fuel bundles in surface monoliths. The principal philosophy behind the work is a sensible one—to shield the fuel adequately for as long as possible while at the same time allowing for possible future retrieval. The volumes of spent fuel that will have to be stored are relatively small: 220,000 tons by the year 2000, or enough to cover a football field to a depth of 13 feet.

At present nearly all the spent fuel from Canadian reactors is being stored at the reactor sites, under 20 feet of water in spacious, swimming-pool-like "storage bays." Only after a year or more of such immersion has the fuel cooled enough to be handled for packaging and transportation to a disposal site. Several alternative methods have been studied for entombing the fuel at the disposal site, but the most recent AECL papers on the subject suggest storage in concrete cylinders lined with lead. In this scheme 222 fuel bundles, which have been cooled in underwater storage for five years, are stacked in a steel cylinder 30 inches in diameter and 11 feet long. The cylinder is welded shut and placed in a concrete canister with walls about 2½ feet thick, for an overall outside size of 7½ feet in diameter by 16 feet high. A layer of lead shot is poured in between the steel cylinder and the concrete walls and then the opening is sealed with a removable concrete plug. The completed canister is then transported to the storage area (a large field with roadways between rows of gravel foundations) where it is placed upright on its foundation, two rows of canisters 15 feet apart between each roadway. The separation of the canisters is necessary to allow for adequate cooling by natural air currents, but the resulting picture is strikingly reminiscent of the rows of long-eared stone monoliths on Easter Island. All of the spent fuel accumulated in Canada up to the year 2000 could be accommodated this way in a plot of about two hundred acres. The minimum life expectancy of each canister has been set at fifty years for accounting purposes, but the actual life would probably be considerably longer, requiring transfer of the spent fuel to new containers perhaps every century. Estimated storage costs, including an allowance for perpetual upkeep expenses, are about $3 per kilogram, for a total spent fuel storage cost by the year 2000 of $300 million.

AECL engineers expect to have this, or some comparable, system in operation by about 1980, unless a decision is taken before then to build a reprocessing plant. In that case, spent fuel would simply be held in storage bays at the reactor site to await shipment to the reprocessing plant. Fission product wastes from the plant could be solidified and stored in much the same way as the intact fuel bundles.

In the meantime, non-fuel solid and liquid wastes associated with nuclear research and power production (such as contaminated water, ion exchange columns, air filters, damaged or obsolete pipes, valves) continue to accumulate and must be disposed of. Most of the disposal work is handled at AECL's Chalk River, Ontario, research establishment, where Canada's reactor program was born. Low-level liquids from laundry and decontamination centres are simply dumped into the river, where they are diluted enough to meet Ministry of the Environment "acceptable" standards. Medium-level liquids, such as the water from spent fuel storage bays and chemicals from laboratories, are sometimes bled into the river a little at a time, or mixed with vermiculite and turned into concrete for burial. But most of these liquids—about 7½ million gallons a year—are pumped into pits dug in the earth, from where they presumably filter into the ground water system. In the light of the evidence that even the smallest amounts of radiation are harmful and of the known tendency of radioactivity to concentrate itself through the food chain like DDT, AECL's liquid disposal methods would seem to leave much to be desired. Only high-level wastes (of which only about 3,600 gallons have been produced in Canada) are kept in "perpetual" storage in stainless steel tanks.

Low-level solids, which are mainly clothing and other com-

113

bustible material, are buried in trenches well above the highest point of the water table at both Chalk River and Whiteshell, Manitoba. About 700 cubic metres a year must be so disposed of. Medium-level solids (wastes which contain more radioactivity but do not require shielded containers for handling) are put in asphalt-lined bunkers of reinforced concrete. When a bunker is filled, it is back-filled with sand and sealed with a concrete cap. About 540 cubic metres are currently disposed of in this way each year. High-level solids including a few fuel bundles are stored in "vertical, water resistant facilities of diameters up to 36 inches and depths of up to 15 feet," according to an AECL report, which goes on to add with rather unsettling redundancy: "The facilities are designed to be waterproof." About 675 of these "waterproof" storage holes have been filled to date at Whiteshell and Chalk River.

Finally, the most dramatic disposal problem (though certainly not the most serious) involves the reactor buildings themselves. Nuclear reactors have a typical life-expectancy of thirty years. Even if they turn out to last much longer than this, and even if it is discovered to be feasible to break through the concrete walls of the containment structures to replace worn-out reactor cores from time to time, the question eventually arises: "What do we do with the building now that it is obsolete?" AECL engineers aren't sure, but they doubt that it could be decontaminated. Probably the buildings will have to be sealed with concrete, fenced off, and left, like the pyramids, as monuments to a civilization.

There is a brighter side to recent developments in nuclear energy, and that is the growing promise of experiments in achieving controlled thermonuclear fusion. A controlled thermonuclear reactor (CTR) would burn deuterium extracted from water (or possibly deuterium and tritium, which is deuterium with an extra neutron in its nucleus) to produce helium, a harmless, inert gas. Only a very small amount of radiation would likely be produced in the process, and because of high operating temperatures a CTR could produce electricity directly, without employing a thermally-polluting steam cycle.

The nuclear fusion process is essentially the opposite of the fission process, in which the nuclei of heavy atoms are split to release energy. In fusion, the nuclei of very light atoms (hydrogen, deuterium or tritium) are joined together or fused to produce a new, heavier atom (helium). As the fusion takes place, large amounts of energy are released. For fusion to occur, the two nuclei must approach one another within distances not much greater than their own diameters; but since they carry the same positive electrical charge and therefore try to repel one another they must be moving at very high speed if they are to have enough energy to get that close together. Such speeds can be induced only by heating the atoms to temperatures reached in the sun itself: the necessary temperature for a deuterium-deuterium fusion, for example, is about 113 million degrees Fahrenheit and for the deuterium-tritium reaction is about 770 million degrees. On earth such temperatures have been achieved only in nuclear explosions, which is why hydrogen, or thermonuclear, bombs use fission bombs as triggers. Of course, atomic bombs cannot be used to initiate a fusion reaction in a power plant, but recently lasers have been developed which are capable of heating small amounts of matter to the required temperatures for brief periods.

Once the fusion process has been initiated, the problem becomes one of how to contain it and prevent it from dying out. Clearly, with temperatures of hundreds of millions of degrees involved, no material structure will do, so scientists have developed a "bottle" of very strong magnetic fields. To date, no one has been able to produce even a laboratory reaction which generated more energy than was consumed in initiating fusion, but researchers in the field confidently expect such an experiment before the end of the decade. If that is the case, one might expect a prototype power plant by the end of the century or even earlier. And then, perhaps, fusion power will fulfil the promises originally made of fission power: a safe, clean, cheap and essentially limitless source of energy. Perhaps.

5.
The Problem of Energy Conservation

The first technologically sophisticated civilizations in the Western world developed in Egypt and the great river valleys of southeastern Europe around the middle of the fourth millennium B.C. It was there that the alluvial flooding taught subsistence farmer-hunters irrigation and enriched the soil so that comfortable surpluses could be produced. Archaeological evidence from Sumeria shows that the cities of this period were centred around the temple: the surplus food was brought there to propitiate what is assumed to have been a powerful and vindictive god. The temple priests, benefactors of the farmers' gifts from the land, became the first leisured class; their leisure time enabled them to develop the various crafts through which they sought to honour the god, and which signalled the true beginnings of civilization—and technological progress. In Egypt the surplus went to the granaries of earthly kings, offered up, archaeologists surmise, out of fear and submission to military might. However, the distinction is less real than apparent, since the kings of Egypt soon came to be regarded as gods incarnate on earth. In any event, the result in the Nile valley was much the same as in the valleys of the Tigris and Euphrates: a well-endowed leisure class was freed to develop and refine technology.

When the scattered remains of our own civilization are unearthed millennia hence by some future archaeologist, he may well ponder over the nature of the particular god we were trying to propitiate. Sifting through the crumbling artifacts of the vast middens that surround our settlements, he will have no doubt of the existence of a technologically advanced leisure class. But he will undoubtedly spend a great deal of time speculating as to what awesome vision could have driven us to offer up such enormous caches of material of all sorts, from plastics to paper to metals, all carefully covered by a layer of soil and marked with enigmatic scratchings on a metal plate: C-I-T-Y D-U-M-P. For it is clear that, if there are to be civilized men on earth in future millennia, the idea of waste of energy and materials on the present scale will be as incomprehensible to them as human sacrifice and bull-leaping are to us.

A religious interpretation would not be entirely inappropriate for the economic system that has led to the creation of such incredible waste. It is a system that puts growth above all other considerations, that assumes that there is no such thing as enough and no such restraint as too much of a good thing. "If it is agreed that economic output is a good thing, it follows by definition that there is not enough of it," states the U.S. President's Council of Economic Advisors in its 1971 report. The Economic Council of Canada, chief economic advisors to the federal government, sees as its most important function advising the government on how to maintain "a high rate of economic growth." Not a "suitable" or "appropriate" rate, but a high rate. Even the Science Council of Canada admits to an unquestioning acceptance of economic growth as a necessary goal: in testimony before the Senate Special Committee on Science Policy in 1970, Science Council chairman O. M. Solandt stated that "the object of the Science Council is to try to understand the impact of science on Canadian society and how we can best use science [to further] the growth and development of the country." One must refer to a report prepared for the Privy Council Office (*Environmental Management* by J. W. Mac-Neill), which states on its frontispiece," . . . although this study is being made available by the government, the views expressed therein are those of the author, and are not necessarily those of the government," to find an admission that economic growth may have its drawbacks:

> The genesis of environmental deterioration is to be found in in-creased population, industrialization and technological innovation and their derived products. Normally these are hailed as indicators of growth and standards of the success of public policy. More people with more money enjoying more mobility and more leisure and pro-ducing and consuming more per person each year represents both individual and collective aspirations.

Yet these same goals require ever-increasing quantities of land, water and raw materials. They result in heavier pressures on the environment at all points, causing more air pollution; more crowding in our cities, on our highways and at our beaches; more automobile junkyards; more land stripped for mining; and more species threatened with extinction. *The costs and benefits of growth are two sides of the same coin.*

Yet even here one waits in vain for the author to ask the obvious question: When do the costs of growth in the GNP outweigh the benefits? The answer to such a question would be put by economists in these terms: The costs outweigh the benefits when the decreasing marginal (extra) benefit of an additional increase in GNP is outweighed by the increasing marginal cost. Governments all over the world spend millions of dollars each year collecting statistics on the marginal benefit as indicated by increases in the money value of goods and services produced— that is, by increases in the GNP. But nowhere does government systematically collect statistics on the marginal costs.

In fact, where information on the costs of coping with unwanted side-effects of growth is available (in terms of land reclamation expenses, money spent to clean up oil spills and reduce air pollution, increased medical expenses and so on) these expenditures are *added* to the GNP, instead of being subtracted as common sense would seem to dictate. Thus, in this system of accounting, the net benefit of growth can never be negative; as formerly free commodities like clean air and unpolluted water become scarce, they acquire an economic price and thereby become part of our stock of wealth, giving us the illusion that we are better off, when in reality we are worse off. The results of this strangely perverse outlook are all around us. When traffic piles up we build new expressways; when crop yields begin to fall off because of soil depletion, we build new fertilizer factories; when airports become congested, we expropriate land to build new ones; when lakes become polluted, we build swimming pools on their shores. And in each case, the GNP goes up, telling us that we are better off than ever before.

There can be no rational explanation for such an uncritical, singleminded, impenitent dedication to growth for growth's sake. It is mysticism, pure and simple. It is in our national interest to continue to foster rapid economic growth. Why? Because.

While there is virtually no statistical evidence available for examination, casual empirical observations would seem to indicate that we may already have reached that point where the marginal utility of growth has been overtaken by the marginal disutility. Current world inflation, caused, evidently, by materials shortages in various rapidly expanding sectors of the economy, lends substantial weight to the argument that further economic growth (in North America at any rate) can only lead to a worsening of the human condition. Leaders of even the most powerful of unions complain that the substantial wage increases they negotiate on behalf of their members seldom, these days, mean a net increase in the workers' standard of living. The wage-earner is on a treadmill; he must run hard just to stay in the same place. And there are other indicators: mental hospitals full to overflowing; endemic violence on city streets; burgeoning alienation resulting from fragmented social structures; decadence in the arts; the evolution of a potent minority counter-culture based on a common revulsion for excessive material wealth.

However, since there is little reason to expect that a consensus on the need to halt or even moderate traditional economic growth will be arrived at in the near future, it is worth exploring some approaches to limiting the use of energy within the present growth-oriented system. None of them represent a solution to the problem, but they may enable us to keep the symptoms under control until the disease itself can be attacked.

In classical economics there are three factors of production: labour, capital and resources (including energy). The achievement of any given rate of growth in an economy can come about through input of these factors in a wide variety of proportions. In a country with a relatively small population, like Canada, growth is realized through large inputs of capital and resources, which compensate for smaller labour inputs. In China and India, the same rate of growth could in theory be achieved by substituting large amounts of labour for scarce capital and resources, particularly energy resources.

Given a situation in which the need to conserve resources is evident, the problem, if growth is to be maintained, is one of substituting the other factors of production for resources. In the industrialized world, where populations in most countries are at, or approaching, zero growth and where unemployment is relatively insignificant, there is little extra labour available for substitution duty, and what there is, is expensive. Which leaves us with capital; in other words, the machinery of production. Put another way, then, the problem is one of how to adapt technology to the new situation of scarce resources. (Although there are distinctions to be made between the two, it is accurate enough here to treat capital and technology as synonymous.)

Although the same lines of reasoning would apply to most other scarce, non-renewable resources, the concern here is with that most crucial of all resources: energy. How can we most effectively substitute technology for dwindling energy reserves? How can we adapt technology to use energy more efficiently and thereby stretch the lifetime of those reserves?

In recent discussions of the energy problem a theme has begun to emerge whose irresistible logic seems destined to give it a role in political discussions in years to come. It is, for a generation of technocrats, an embarrassingly simple truth: haste makes waste. Or, put in less emotionally loaded terms, increased speed and intensity (or power) in economic processes such as manufacturing, transportation and agriculture, can be achieved only through increasing energy subsidies.

For example, between 1950 and 1970 the amount of energy used by aircraft to carry passengers or freight over any given distance doubled, as airlines traded energy for speed. Freight shipped by air currently eats up over fifty times as much energy as freight carried more slowly by sea. Tests conducted by General Motors on cars with large displacement engines showed that an increase in cruising speed from 50 to 70 miles per hour requires an energy subsidy of up to 25 per cent in the form of increased gasoline consumption.

To put it another way, the amount of *power* derived from an energy source depends not only on the energy, but also on the length of time involved. Power, strictly defined, means this:

$$\text{power} = \frac{\text{energy}}{\text{time}}$$

So that energy = power × time. A gallon of gasoline contains a specific, measurable amount of energy. But the amount of power to be derived from it depends on how quickly or intensively it is consumed. It might produce five horsepower for two or three hours in a motorcycle engine, or it might produce 60,000 horsepower for a second or two in a jetliner.

Professor Stephen Berry of Chicago University has demonstrated, through an exhaustive thermodynamic or energy analysis of the American automobile industry, that 80 per cent of the energy expended on production lines represents a subsidy over the amount of energy theoretically required, with present technology, to put a car together: 80 per cent of the energy used is wasted because of the haste with which the car is produced. This waste is permitted to occur because immediate profits to the automobile manufacturers rise with the speed of production. The cost of energy is so low—so unrealistically low, it seems clear—that the waste incurred deflates profits only insignificantly. Going a step further back into the manufacturing process, Professor Berry and associate Margaret Fels analysed the energy consumption patterns of the factories producing the various materials that go into the making of an automobile; they then compared these figures with estimates of the amount of energy that would be consumed in the various refining and fabricating processes if existing technology were used to maximize energy savings. They concluded that, due to considerations such as speed and intensity, thirty-five times as much energy is consumed in the production of the materials used in the manufacture of an automobile as is ideally necessary. Once again, the waste is allowed to occur because it makes economic sense in terms of our present short-sighted system of accounting.

There is an obvious dichotomy revealed by these studies between economic cost and energetic cost. The first reflects the value society currently places on the product; the second expresses the magnitude of the irretrievable loss of a portion of our finite supplies of energy. As the shock and confusion with which we awakened to the current energy shortages has made clear, the economic valuation we have placed on energy resources turns out to be wildly inaccurate over anything but the shortest of terms. If this were not the case, shortages would only develop gradually over long periods of time. As Stephen Berry points out: "If the economists in the market-place were to determine their shortages by looking further into the future, these estimates would come closer and closer to the estimates made by their colleagues, the thermodynamicists. . . . For the ultimate long-range planner, economic and thermodynamic analyses are equivalent."

It is also clear from thermodynamic analyses that (given current or foreseeable technology) energy subsidy is closely related to the rate of economic growth. Rapid growth takes place only at the expense of increased energy subsidy or waste.

Nowhere are the costs of speed and power more obvious than in agriculture, which has undergone a dramatic change in North America over the past thirty years. Not only has the average size of farms increased enormously (forcing millions of small farmers into the cities and towns) but the amount of capital equipment in use has also soared. Although total acreage in production has changed little, the total value of farm machinery in use in the United States since 1950 has tripled to more than $34 billion. In Canada, the value of farm machinery in use continues to grow at about 5 per cent a year.

The mechanization of farms and the increased use of industry-produced chemicals has not, however, been without hitches. Numerous problems have arisen, each of which has been temporarily solved only through the application of more sophisticated technology. For example, the mechanically efficient practice of seeding huge areas to the same crop has increased pest problems by removing natural controls; the answer has been increased application of pesticides with power-driven dusters and sprayers. Nor have these solutions proven entirely satisfactory, even in the short run. The evolution of pesticide-resistant "superbugs" has been well documented, as have disastrous population explosions among species released from the predator-prey cycle by man's extermination of some natural enemy. Hybrid crop strains introduced to increase per acre yields of grains have escalated soil depletion with their more extensive root networks and aggressive feeding characteristics. To counteract this, farmers have greatly increased their use of synthetic fertilizers. This has led to enormous water pollution problems; it has also, in at least some cases, meant a reduction of the protein content of the grain. Low-yield Indian corn grown in the United States prior to World War One showed a protein content of 12 to 15 per cent. Extensive hybridization beginning around 1940 resulted in a protein content in

1950 of between 8 and 9 per cent. By 1956 protein yields had in some instances fallen as low as 5 per cent. Agronomists have called the effect the "inverse nitrogen law": the more nitrogen found in a crop, the less its protein yield is likely to be. To make up for the falling protein content of the corn, livestock men who fed corn to their cattle began purchasing fish meal protein supplements manufactured mainly from anchovies caught off Peru. (According to some sources, the United States imports enough fish protein to eliminate one-half the protein deficiency prevalent among the people of South America.)

Professor Michael Perelman of the University of California has done a rough thermodynamic analysis of these trends in North American agriculture; the results are startling. He estimates that the five million farm tractors in the United States annually consume about eight billion gallons of fuel, which contain the equivalent of about 1,000 trillion BTU of heat value. The American population consumes in food each year about 876 trillion BTU, making the energy value of food consumed only slightly lower than the energy used by farm tractors alone. Modern farms also consume a large amount of electricity: in the United States, the equivalent of 350 trillion BTU of fuel each year. But total farm energy consumption is much higher even than the sum of tractor and electricity consumption. A paper published by the American Association for the Advancement of Science puts total annual consumption at more than 10 million BTU per acre, and even this does not take into account the energy required to produce the farm equipment or to store and distribute the food. Professor Perelman estimates from this that it takes about 150 gallons of gasoline a year to feed a single American from domestic farm products; the gasoline contains about five times as much energy as is contained in the food produced. Had he included energy consumed in fertilizer production, the ratio would have been even higher. In 1969 U.S. farms used about 7.5 million tons of nitrogen fertilizer, the production of which consumed in heat value the equivalent of 1.5 billion gallons of gasoline, or about eight gallons for each American being fed. And nitrogen makes up only about one-fifth of total fertilizer use.

By contrast, it has been estimated that Chinese wet rice agriculture can produce more than 53 BTU of energy for each BTU of human energy expended by the farmer. This ratio is almost exactly the inverse of the one experienced in American agriculture. Looked at from this point of view, Chinese wet rice agriculture is by far the more efficient.

Perelman's point is that agriculture in North America has the potential to be a *producer* of energy rather than one of the economy's largest consumers. After all, crops store immense amounts of energy from the sun. A description of energy use on a Chinese farm provided by the *Peking Review* lends weight to his contention. In North America stubble, for instance, is generally either burned or ploughed under. In China it was used in several manufacturing processes; it was also burned in cook stoves, the heat from which was ducted through large blocks of subsoil which served as (pre-warmed) beds for the occupants of the house. When bacterial action, accelerated by the heat, began crumbling the soil blocks, they were spread on the land as fertilizer. While no one would suggest that a return by the North American farmer to that degree of energy-consciousness, or to the implied degree of labour-intensiveness in production, would be desirable, the example nonetheless reinforces the conclusion that there is enormous potential for energy-saving in our system of agriculture. One could well speculate whether a reversion to the pattern of smaller, family-operated mixed farms and the resultant increased labour input would not, in terms of thermodynamic efficiency (and therefore in terms of long-range economic efficiency), be advisable. Certainly, there seems to be little serious dissent to the argument that the virtual disappearance of the small family farm has been a sociological and humanistic disaster. No one has better or more movingly described the process than John Steinbeck in *The Grapes of Wrath*:

> The man sitting in the iron seat [of the tractor] did not look like a man; gloved, goggled, rubber mask over nose and mouth, he was a part of the monster, a robot in the seat. The thunder of the cylinders sounded through the country became one with the air and the earth, so that earth and air muttered in sympathetic vibration. The driver could not control it—straight across country it went, cutting through a dozen farms and straight back. A twitch at the controls could swerve the cat', but the driver's hands could not twitch because the monster that built the tractor, the monster that sent the tractor out, had somehow got into the driver's hands, into his brain and muscle,

had goggled him and muzzled him—goggled his mind, muzzled his speech, goggled his perception, muzzled his protest. He could not see the land as it was, he could not smell the land as it smelled; his feet did not stamp the clods or feel the warmth and power of the earth. He sat in an iron seat and stepped on iron pedals. He could not cheer or beat or curse or encourage the extension of his power, and because of this he could not cheer or whip or curse or encourage himself. He did not know or own or trust or beseech the land. If a seed dropped did not germinate, it was nothing. If the young thrusting plant withered in drought or drowned in a flood of rain, it was no more to the driver than to the tractor. . . . The driver sat in his iron seat and he was proud of the straight lines he did not will, proud of the tractor he did not own or love, proud of the power he could not control. And when that crop grew, and was harvested, no man had crumbled a hot clod in his fingers and let the earth sift past his fingertips. No man had touched the seed, or lusted for the growth. Men ate what they had not raised, had no connection with the bread. The land bore under iron, and under iron gradually died; for it was not loved or hated, it had no prayers or curses.

Former U.S. Secretary of Agriculture Clifford Hardin effusively reported, in the 1970 U.S. Department of Agriculture *Yearbook*: "Using a modern feeding system for broilers, one man can take care of 60,000 to 75,000 chickens. One man in a modern feedlot can now take care of 5,000 cattle. One man with a mechanized system can operate a dairy enterprise of 50 to 60 milk cows. Agriculture, in short, does an amazing job of producing food."

The *Canada Yearbook* echoes this paean to efficiency: "The Canadian farmer continues to become more efficient in the production of the raw material for food and feed to fulfill much of the requirements of the Canadian population and assist with those of other countries. . . ." Noted in passing is the fact that " . . . farm operating expenses and depreciation charges advanced, partly because of the higher prices paid by farmers for goods and services. Shipments of manufactured livestock and poultry feeds increased again and prices also rose. Petroleum product prices and expenditures for farm machinery and parts were up as were wage rates in agriculture. The farmers' outlay for debt servicing continued upward." Perhaps it is time for a new definition of "efficiency".

While the concept of thermodynamic efficiency as it relates to the economics of dwindling energy supplies has been bubbling away in the academic and scientific journals, growing and developing, the public's attention has been directed mainly to more concrete proposals for energy conservation. And the two areas with the most obvious potential for savings are buildings and transportation.

Construction and operation of buildings consume well over half the total energy production of the United States and Canada. It has been frequently estimated that as much as 25 per cent of that energy could be saved with more care and less haste in design and construction. Structural engineers in Canada and the United States have argued for several years that with a more labour-intensive approach to building construction—with more care in the building of forms and mixing of concrete, and in placing steel correctly, for instance—very substantial savings in energy and materials could result. Prefabricated buildings, in which each component is carefully designed and constructed away from the building site, often require half as much in the way of materials (and, consequently, much less in the way of energy used to produce and transport the materials) as buildings constructed on the site. The waste related to site-constructed buildings is a result of substitution of excess materials to compensate for a time-and-labour-saving lack of precision in design and fabrication. For instance, it is to the builder's advantage to put a lot of relatively cheap concrete in a hastily designed and built form rather than to pay a craftsman for the extra time involved in carefully designing and building a mould that would permit the use of less concrete to do the same job.

Substitution of materials that consume less energy in fabrication for other, more energy-intensive materials would result in further savings. Aluminum, the currently fashionable skin for office towers, uses up five times as much energy in the fabrication process as steel. Even given its extra weight (but reduced thickness), substitution of stainless steel for aluminum for the skin of a typical office tower could result in an overall energy saving of two-thirds. And, as a rule, plastics and other synthetics used in construction require more energy to produce than the natural materials they replace.

Lighting is an area of notorious energy waste in buildings, and since it accounts for 24 per cent of electricity use in the United

States and slightly more than one-quarter of total electricity use in Canada, it is a potential area of significant saving. In North America, lighting standards followed in the construction industry are established by the Illuminating Engineering Society (IES). Since 1959, IES-recommended light levels have, on average, tripled. There has been virtually no outside scientific corroboration of the society's contention that contrasts in interior lighting of more than 25 per cent in intensity are disturbing or inefficient. Nor is there any substantial support for the IES rule that efficiency in performing visual tasks is proportional to the intensity of diffuse light. In fact, recent independent studies have indicated that a too-bright, shadowless room causes fatigue and anxiety in its occupants, and that light levels of 10 to 15 foot-candles are adequate for normal reading, while 20 to 25 foot-candles are sufficient for fine distinctions. (Foot-candle is a measure of light intensity per square foot.) The IES-recommended level for libraries is 70 foot-candles; for classrooms, 60 foot-candles; for drafting rooms, 100 foot-candles. The fact that the IES is supported entirely by the lighting industry has led, in view of its recommendations, to charges that its standards are self-serving. Unfortunately, IES standards have long since been entrenched in official building codes and design criteria in many states and provinces, and where no standards have been established by authorities, engineers routinely employ the IES handbook.

The approximately 50 per cent saving in lighting energy that could be made by simply lowering intensities to reasonable levels could be amplified by a return to more selective switching arrangements and away from the current trend in commercial buildings to "one floor, one switch," a policy that is particularly wasteful in buildings which provide large windows for daylight illumination around each floor's perimeter. Reduced light intensities would also lessen the need for air conditioning, required in many buildings even in cool weather to compensate for heat generated by lights.

Electric heating in homes and commercial buildings continues to expand its share of the North American space-heating market, principally because it reduces the initial construction costs for the speculative builder (who has little interest in long-range maintenance costs). But electricity provides heat at an efficiency of only

30 per cent, while a gas or oil furnace operates at an efficiency of 70 to 80 per cent of the heat potential of the fuel consumed. To their credit, many state and provincial power utilities insist on superior insulation in buildings using electric heating, but any savings made here have, in the past, been more than compensated for by the utilities' deliberate promotion of "all-electric living." Happily, most of these promotion programs were hastily cancelled in the face of 1974's fuel shortages; by that time about one-third of all new homes being constructed in North America were being equipped with electric heating, and the trend was strongly upward. (In 1966 home heating accounted for one per cent of electricity use in Canada. Government projections of current trends put the figure at 11 per cent by 1980 and 36 per cent by 1990.)

Transportation, with its 25 per cent share of total North American energy consumption, is another area where obvious short-term savings can be made. The deficiencies of the private American automobile are well-known; huge savings of gasoline would result immediately from a shift in production from the typical two-ton, disaster-prone Detroit behemoth to smaller, lighter cars on the European model. As well, numerous proposals have been made for replacement of the gasoline-burning internal combustion engine with more efficient power plants like the gas turbine, external combustion "steam" engines of various types, electric motors powered by various kinds of batteries, and a whole range of hybrid systems combining two or more new types of propulsion. The initial drive behind these development projects was provided by the problem of smog: the increased efficiency claimed for all of these engines is seen in terms of the completeness with which the fuel is burned. The more complete combustion is, the fewer polluting residues are expelled through the exhaust pipe. However, it is by no means certain that these alternative engines would be significantly more efficient thermodynamically— in terms of passenger or freight-miles per BTU—than current models. It would be difficult to justify any large-scale conversion in the automotive industry to a new power plant unless substantial increases in energy efficiency can be expected in the total life of the vehicle, from manufacture to use by the consumer to ultimate recycling.

In this connection, it should be noted in passing that Stephen

Berry's analysis of the automobile industry has led him to predict that it would take an increase in initial energy expenditure of only 15 per cent to manufacture cars that would last three times as long as current American models; this would mean that the manufacturing cost in terms of vehicle-miles or vehicle-years would be just 38 per cent of the current cost. Clearly it is in our long-range economic interest to design and build such long-lived vehicles in the future. Moreover, it seems likely that similar savings could be achieved in many other sectors of the manufacturing industry. The main short-term economic cost would be in redistribution of labour to accommodate the implied increase in design tolerances and improved quality control inspection.

Whichever engine is ultimately chosen to power the automobile of the future, it will have to be provided with an easily transportable fuel supply. Hydrogen is often touted as the automotive fuel of the future, in large part because of its clean-burning characteristics. When burned with oxygen, the only residue to combustion is water. Moreover, though today's main source of hydrogen is natural gas, hydrogen can be produced from water. However, the process of separating hydrogen from water is one which consumes large amounts of electrical energy; even if there was ample electrical generating capacity available, pollution problems like waste heat generation by power plants would soon impose limits on the fuel's production. Another advantage seen by proponents of hydrogen as a fuel of the future is the fact that it can be burned in today's cars with only minor modifications to the engine. But a hydrogen-burning American Motors Gremlin modified by students at the University of California could carry only enough of the fuel to drive the car about sixty miles. Potential storage capacity is greatly increased if the hydrogen is liquefied, but to keep the gas in a liquid state means cooling it to −423 degrees Fahrenheit, just 37 degrees above absolute zero. There is a limit to how long hydrogen can be kept liquid even in expensive cryogenic Dewar tanks, similar in principle to the common thermos bottle. Another hydrogen-storing method being explored is metal hydrides. Certain metals, such as magnesium and titanium, can be infused with hydrogen, which can later be released as a gas by heat. But there is not sufficient heat in the car's exhaust to release the gas; furthermore, the metals contain only about 2 per cent hydrogen by weight, so metal storage could be expected to add three hundred pounds or more to the weight of a conventional car.

A far more promising petroleum substitute is methanol, or "wood alcohol." It, too, can be burned in standard internal combustion engines. In fact, researchers have found that diluting gasoline in the tank of any standard car with up to 15 per cent methanol causes marked improvements in performance and mileage and a significant reduction in exhaust emissions, with no discernible increase in engine wear. A standard gasoline-burning automobile can be converted to burn pure methanol by altering the fuel-air mixture, recycling more exhaust heat and providing for cold starts. Estimated cost of such conversion is in the neighbourhood of $100 per vehicle.

But perhaps the most exciting aspect of methanol as a potential replacement for gasoline is the fact that it can be produced from methane gas (by partial oxidation with water); methane is produced biologically by the decomposition of organic wastes such as compost, sewage and animal manure. Methane gas itself can be (and has been) used to fuel automobiles, trucks and buses (notably, Stockholm's famous "chicken-shit bus"); however, gas storage problems similar to those experienced with hydrogen limit the range of a methane-fuelled standard-sized automobile to about fifty miles. Conversion of the gas to liquid methanol makes the fuel much more practical.

A recent patent has also proposed production of methanol as a by-product of combustion of municipal garbage in a high-temperature, oxygen-fed cooker. If all North American garbage were to be disposed of in this way, the methanol produced would fill about 8 per cent of total transport fuel requirements.

Methanol can also be synthesized from virtually any carbonaceous fuel, from coal to natural gas. And, as its colloquial name implies, it can be produced from wood (for example, the "slash" waste from logging) and other vegetable matter. It can be obtained from renewable resources. It is estimated that less than a quarter of the continent's commercial forest, operated as energy plantations, could fuel all our thermal electric power stations.

And finally, it should be noted for future reference that methane can be converted to electricity in fuel cells, thus providing a silent, non-polluting, portable source of electrical energy. Unfortunately fuel cells are, for the moment at least, extremely expensive to manufacture.

In view of the manifest advantages of the fuel as a replacement for petroleum, it is puzzling that more of the billions of dollars earmarked for energy research in North America have not been directed to exploring the feasibility of large-scale methane production.

TABLE 4   RELATIVE IMPORTANCE OF VARIOUS FORMS OF TRANSPORT IN
         U.S. AND CANADA IN 1970

Service	Intercity passenger miles (%)		Intercity freight ton/miles (%)	
	Canada	U.S.	Canada	U.S.
Car or truck	82	87	10	19
Intercity bus	7	2	x	x
Railway	4	1	41	35
Airline	7	10	x	x
Water	x	x	25 ⎫	46
Pipeline	x	x	24 ⎭	

x   less than 1%

Because it is compatible with gasoline as a fuel, it could be introduced into the economy gradually, without sudden dislocations. Even produced from lignite costing $2 a ton, it would cost less than gasoline, at current prices. Produced from trash, sewage and agricultural wastes, its net cost could well be close to zero, if environmental considerations are properly taken into the accounting system. It can be stored in conventional storage tanks and transported in conventional tank cars and pipelines. It burns with a clean flame comparable to that of natural gas. It is miscible with water in any proportion, so spills are quickly dispersed. In short, it is the most environmentally sound fuel currently available to us.

Short of redesigning our vehicles and shifting to methanol or some other alternative to petroleum fuels, there is much that can be done to conserve energy simply through redistribution of transport among existing carriers. Tables 4 and 5 indicate clearly that increased use of mass transit facilities like trains and buses

TABLE 5

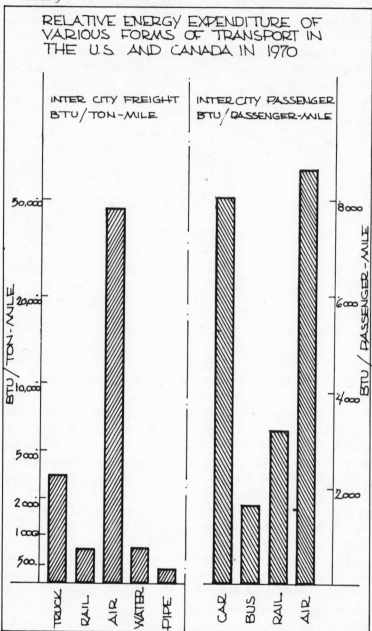

RELATIVE ENERGY EXPENDITURE OF VARIOUS FORMS OF TRANSPORT IN THE U.S AND CANADA IN 1970

INTER CITY FREIGHT BTU/TON-MILE

INTER CITY PASSENGER BTU/PASSENGER-MILE

and less use of automobiles and aircraft would result in a much more efficient use of fuel. The savings to be had through increased use of mass transit within cities are just as obvious and substantial. Unfortunately the trends in transportation as currently projected are not encouraging: in Canada between 1958 and 1969 aircraft accounted for 5.4 per cent of total energy use in transportation; by 1969 this had risen to 7.9 per cent and Department of Energy, Mines and Resources projections place the figure for 1990 at 20 per cent. Highway users (principally cars and trucks) used 67 per cent of the total in 1958; by 1969 this had risen to 76 per cent and the projection for 1990 is 69.5 per cent. Rail transport's share of total transport energy use actually fell between 1958 and 1969, from 17 per cent to 7.3 per cent. The projection for 1990 is an even lower 4.5 per cent. Water transport figures are similarly discouraging: 9.8 per cent in 1958, 8.8 per cent in 1969 and 6.2 per cent projected for 1990.

Figures such as these make obvious the kind of policy decisions that must be taken to maximize energy conservation in the economy, and they give some indication of the size of the savings that might be expected. However, there is a danger of becoming immersed in such data on specific conservation issues and failing to keep the larger picture in perspective. A study of conservation policies and their effect carried out in the United States by the Office of Emergency Preparedness (OEP) in 1972 can be of some help in getting back to earth. The study reported in detail on three areas judged to provide the greatest potential for energy conservation: the installation of improved insulation in both new and old houses and the use of more efficient air conditioners; a shift of intercity freight from trucks to rail, of intercity passengers from automobiles to motorized mass transit, increased mileage for cars and an improvement in urban freight handling systems through consolidation and containerization; and the introduction of more efficient industrial processes and equipment. Many of the OEP's suggestions for conservation in these three areas have been criticized as unrealistic, and estimates of likely savings often seem optimistic. But even if the OEP's estimated savings could be realized by 1980, there would be no reduction in consumption of U.S. domestic energy resources, and projected imports would be reduced by only about two-thirds. Given current projections of energy requirements for 1980, this would mean that the time when U.S. oil imports are expected to reach 10 million barrels a day (or half of total consumption) would be delayed just five years—from 1980 to 1985. In other words, conservation efforts themselves cannot, given yearly increases in over-all energy consumption, do more than delay for a very few years the level of energy consumption estimated as being reached at some earlier date without new conservation measures. Even if one were to add a complete conversion of American transportation to the use of methanol by 1980 into the OEP proposals, the 10-million-barrel-a-day import plateau would be pushed only about five more years into the future, to 1990.

Clearly, something more than simple conservation will be required if we are to do more than just delay by a few short years the ultimate and definitive energy crisis, the day when we run out of fossil fuels. New sources of energy—solar, fusion, geo-thermal—offer one solution to the problem. But then, the old limiting factor of energy resource reserves is merely exchanged for an even more frightening limit in the form of unpredictable, but nonetheless certain, ecological catastrophe in the form of inadvertent climate modification, disruption of the oxygen cycle or some other man-induced breakdown of the global ecosystem resulting from continued economic growth in a waste-saturated environment. And it is by no means certain which of these two limits would be reached first.

All of which brings us back to the question of growth. Ultimately, growth in energy consumption must be reduced to zero. Environmental considerations make this true even if we are fortunate enough to find the perfect, non-polluting source of energy, since continued growth in energy use implies increased pollution by users and accelerated non-fuel resource depletion. Restrictions in the growth of energy consumption would obviously have reper-cussions throughout the economy, but whether these would lead to a decline in standards of living is by no means certain. The ratio of energy consumption to GNP in Canada has been falling more or less steadily since the depression years, due to in-creases in efficiency. There is no reason to believe that further increases in thermodynamic efficiency could not cause a continu-

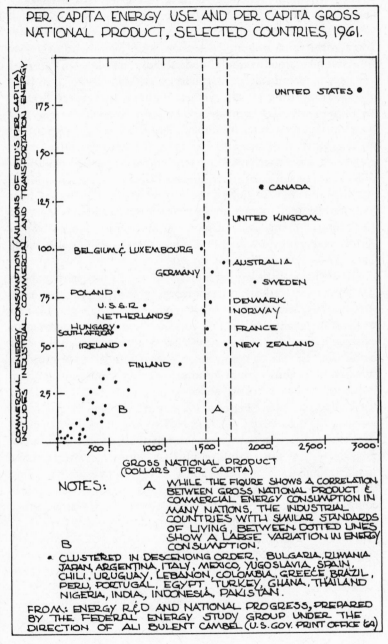

PER CAPITA ENERGY USE AND PER CAPITA GROSS NATIONAL PRODUCT, SELECTED COUNTRIES, 1961.

NOTES:

A — WHILE THE FIGURE SHOWS A CORRELATION BETWEEN GROSS NATIONAL PRODUCT & COMMERCIAL ENERGY CONSUMPTION IN MANY NATIONS, THE INDUSTRIAL COUNTRIES WITH SIMILAR STANDARDS OF LIVING, BETWEEN DOTTED LINES SHOW A LARGE VARIATION IN ENERGY CONSUMPTION.

B — CLUSTERED IN DESCENDING ORDER, BULGARIA, RUMANIA, JAPAN, ARGENTINA, ITALY, MEXICO, YUGOSLAVIA, SPAIN, CHILI, URUGUAY, LEBANON, COLOMBIA, GREECE, BRAZIL, PERU, PORTUGAL, EGYPT, TURKEY, GHANA, THAILAND, NIGERIA, INDIA, INDONESIA, PAKISTAN.

FROM: ENERGY R&D AND NATIONAL PROGRESS, PREPARED BY THE FEDERAL ENERGY STUDY GROUP UNDER THE DIRECTION OF ALI BULENT CAMBEL (U.S. GOV. PRINT OFFICE 6A)

ation of this trend, thereby reducing the effect of cut-backs in energy consumption on the GNP. Certainly, it would seem that substantial reductions in energy consumption could be undertaken without causing any net decrease in GNP, though the rate of economic growth would undoubtedly be slowed. Figure 4 provides further evidence that energy use and economic welfare are far from being closely related. It shows that, while Britain, Belgium, Australia, Germany, Denmark, Norway, France and New Zealand had GNP's (in dollars per capita) within 10 per cent of each other, their per capita energy consumption for industry, commerce and transportation (excluding household and miscellaneous uses) varied much more widely, between 110 million BTU (Britain) and 45 million BTU (New Zealand). The contrast between Sweden and Canada, which share nearly identical standards of living, is even more striking: Sweden's per capita commercial energy consumption is less than 80 million BTU, while Canada's is close to 130 million BTU.

The position of the United States—almost off the chart at about 180 million BTU—leads unavoidably to the deeper and more speculative question of the relationship between energy use and GNP and the quality of life. Is it reasonable to argue, to choose an extreme example, that Americans live a life that is 360 per cent better than the life of the average New Zealander, as the energy consumption figures could be interpreted as suggesting (and as President Nixon, for one, chose to interpret them)? Is life in the United States any better *at all* than it is in New Zealand—or Sweden, or Belgium, or Canada or Norway? Is there *any* necessary relationship between energy consumption, beyond a certain minimum level, and the quality of life? Or between GNP (beyond a similar minimum level) and quality of life? These are questions that have not yet begun to be asked in government circles in most countries. They will have to be answered before any lasting solution to the energy crisis can be found.

Appendix 1:
An Approach to Achieving
the Steady State

One way of approaching transition to a steady-state economy may be through enactment and rigid enforcement of legislation requiring environmental impact assessments of all governmental actions which significantly affect the quality of the environment. In Canada, no such legislation exists; the few impact statements that have been prepared have been undertaken on a strictly ad hoc basis as a result of public pressure, usually well after the project concerned is well under way (if not already completed). In the United States, there is the National Environmental Policy Act (NEPA), which has recently made it possible for conservation groups to halt work on undertakings such as the trans-Alaska pipeline, a north Florida canal linking the Atlantic with the Gulf of Mexico and the granting of offshore oil and gas leases, pending preparation of environmental impact statements. The potential power of NEPA is tremendous, affecting as it does the whole region of federal involvement in the nation's economic processes, including those areas which determine the output of goods and services, investment and capital formation.

Until recently, NEPA has been interpreted by the courts as being merely an environmental full-disclosure act, applicable only to specific government-sanctioned or government-sponsored projects having a physical effect on the environment. When an impact statement is prepared for, say, a new nuclear power station, it has long since been decided, on the basis of projected energy demand and various economic considerations, that the station should be built because it will serve progress and economic growth. The NEPA-required environmental cost-benefit analysis, then, is weighted in favour of the applicant by prior acceptance of the necessity of growth and progress.

But lately judges and lawyers both inside and outside the courts have been asking whether NEPA can and should be interpreted as proper authority to ask whether the stated need or presumed benefit of a project has been created by prior government economic policies that were not subjected to NEPA cost-benefit analysis. The argument is that the federal government's exercise of fiscal, monetary and tax powers all have an obvious and significant effect on the environment and as such should be subject to review under NEPA. If policies of government agencies contribute to growth of highway transport, and that growth makes necessary construction of a new highway, then government policy weights any cost-benefit analysis in favour of the highway, as opposed to any alternative that might be suggested. So the government agencies' transport policies should also be subject to environmental impact assessment.

This point of view was accepted in part when the United States Supreme Court refused to stay an injunction issued by a lower court to prevent the Interstate Commerce Commission from imposing a freight surcharge on scrap materials transported for recycling, without first filing an impact statement on the effect of the surcharge. Opponents of the surcharge successfully argued that it would result in increased environmental degradation by discouraging recycling, even though the surcharge itself had no direct physical impact on the environment.

Lawyer Irving Like, author of the New York State Conservation Bill of Rights, argues:

> It is essential that the NEPA ... be applied to the federal economic policies which precede and have a cause-effect relationship with projects further downstream in the planning or performance stages. If the NEPA cost-benefit analysis is applied at this earlier stage of the federal government's intervention in the economy, it will provide clearer insights on how to manage the problem of harmonizing growth and development with the protection of the environment. It will stimulate debate on how U.S. natural resources can best be allocated, what our national priorities should be, what the optimum size and composition of the GNP is, the broad alternatives to particular economic policies, and what economic theories and models are best suited to managing the nation's productive machine to achieve the objectives of full employment, a high standard of living and a sound economy, compatible with ecological constraints and resource limitations.

Such a policy would require that a nation's most influential economic agencies—the Federal Reserve in the United States and the Bank of Canada in Canada—consider both the costs and benefits of the current policy of unlimited economic growth, and examine carefully the alternatives to this policy and their respective costs and benefits. Policies could then be devised which would allow the central bank to encourage development taking place along environmentally sound lines, and discourage development outside these lines. By acting to protect the environment, the central banks would also be acting to serve the interest of the economy as their legislative mandates require of them; but they would be taking a longer-range view than has been their habit. Economic and environmental considerations may frequently seem to be at variance in the short term, but they invariably coincide in the long run.

The effect of legislation like NEPA and any similar code that may be introduced in Canada should clearly not be to turn over to the courts the power to oversee a government's economic policy-making. It should rather be to provide assurance to the public that alternatives to the policy of maximizing the growth of GNP are being considered, and secondly, to spur public debate as to what the best alternatives to such a policy might be. The need for a forum for such debate is made particularly urgent by the abject failure of political parties in both the United States and Canada to tackle the subject.

Appendix 2:
Oil Shale in the United States

Canadians have a tendency to think of Alberta's tar sands as the only resource of its kind, but there are others, and some of them are even larger. (None, however, is currently being exploited for synthetic crude oil.) The Orinoco Tar Belt deposit in Venezuela is thought to contain as much as 600 billion barrels of bitumen, and little-explored deposits in the Llanos area of Colombia may hold a trillion barrels. However, in both cases the depth of overburden is too great to permit strip mining, so less efficient in situ recovery processes will have to be used when these deposits are eventually opened up to commercial exploitation. Other smaller tar sands deposits are to be found at La Brea, Trinidad (60 million barrels), Derna, Rumania (25 million barrels) and Cheildag, USSR (24 million barrels).

In the United States major tar sands deposits are confined to the state of Utah, in the "Tar Sand Triangle," P. R. Spring, Sunnyside, Circle Cliffs and Asphalt Ridge regions. Total bitumen content of these deposits is thought to be between 17.7 and 27.6 billion barrels. Once again the overburden is too deep to permit strip mining, ranging as it does from 250 feet in the P. R. Spring deposit to more than 2,000 feet in the large Tar Sand Triangle deposit. And there are other complications: proposals for national parks, national monuments and recreational areas cover most of the spectacularly beautiful country overlying the Circle Cliffs and Tar Sand Triangle deposits, uses that are clearly incompatible with oil recovery. Given the growing strength of the environmental lobby and the critical shortage of recreational land in the United States, there is good reason to question whether any substantial fraction of these reserves will be exploited in the foreseeable future. Availability of water is another stumbling block in arid Utah: in situ recovery operations consume enormous volumes of water, little of which is recoverable for recycling.

Because of these and other difficulties associated with development of tar sands in the United States, oil companies have shown increasing interest in oil shale deposits in Colorado, Wyoming and Utah. One company, Occidental Petroleum, has estimated that these deposits (perhaps one-sixth of the world total) contain more than 1.8 trillion barrels of oil. The same company announced late in 1973 that it had developed an in situ extraction process which would allow removal of 50 per cent or more of the recoverable oil found in a deposit without significant damage to the surface environment. The process involves detonating conventional explosives underground to create large pockets of crushed shale. A natural-gas-ignited fire is then started in the pocket, with air for combustion being pumped down from the surface. The heat from the combustion separates the oil from the rock, and it is pumped to the surface for storage. According to Occidental, the costs involved in such an operation are relatively low, an initial investment of $100 million bringing a production level of 100,000 barrels a day. Commercial in situ oil shale plants will likely be in operation before the end of the decade if the company's initial optimism about the process proves justified. It is to be hoped that it is justified, since the alternative method of exploitation of these vast reserves involves literally tearing down mountain ranges in a process which recovers from 5 to 100 gallons of oil from a ton of crushed rock.

If they can be exploited economically, the American oil shales hold a huge potential for future energy production; if it is assumed that one-third of the resource proves commercially exploitable (given both environmental and economic restraints), and that 50 per cent of the bitumen in that one-third is recovered, and further, that the bitumen-to-synthetic crude production ratio is 70 per cent, a total production of about 210 billion barrels of synthetic crude oil could ultimately be expected. (This compares favourably with the ultimate Alberta tar sands potential of some 250 billion barrels.) But it must be borne in mind that, so great is the thirst for energy, if present consumption trends continue even this huge resource could represent a mere ten-year supply for the United States oil market by the year 2000. It's a sobering thought.

Appendix 3:
Everything You *Always*
Wanted To Know
About Energy in Canada

A do-it-yourself kit for prospective energy analysts.

Next to citizens of the United States, Canadians are the world's heaviest per capita users of energy (Figure A.3). Each Canadian uses, on average, the equivalent of the energy contained in 55 barrels of oil each year. That's equivalent to about 33,000 kilowatt hours of electricity or 330,000 cubic feet of natural gas. In the past twenty-five years, energy consumption in Canada has tripled (Figure A.1), and it continues to grow at a rate of 4.3 per cent a year, for a doubling time of about sixteen years. Currently, oil and gas fill about two-thirds of Canada's energy demands, up from about one-quarter twenty-five years ago. Over the past twenty-five years, coal's share of the market has declined from half to about one-tenth. Hydroelectricity has held more or less constant at one-quarter of the market since the late 1950s. It is interesting to note that wood and nuclear energy currently serve roughly equal portions of Canada's energy demands, although nuclear energy's share is rapidly increasing and may match hydroelectric output by the turn of the century.

One of the nation's major industries, energy production in 1972 was valued at $5 billion and had a favourable trade balance of $630 million, compared with a deficit of $300 million twelve years earlier. In 1972 the industry accounted for nearly one-fifth of total capital investment in Canada. And investment will continue to increase with such enormously expensive projects as the James Bay hydro development, the Mackenzie Valley gas and oil transportation systems and ultimately pipeline or other transport facilities for the high Arctic.

By 2000 Canada's energy needs are likely to be more than four times those of today (all things being equal); per capita consumption among a population of 35 million by that year would be 2.7 times that of 1970 (Figure A.4).

Individually, Canada's major energy industries look like this:

COAL

The developing shortages of energy resources over the past few years have led to a major resurgence in Canada's coal industry, a sector that had been in a depressed state for more than twenty years as a result of discoveries of oil and gas in western Canada in the late 1940s, competition from cheap American coal, and high transportation costs. The renewed interest in Canada's extensive coal deposits does not result exclusively from the world's growing demand for energy, however: sources of metallurgical coal for steel production in Japan, Europe and the United States are becoming expensive relative to metallurgical coal mined in Canada, and there has been a resultant increase in exports of this product to these markets. Japanese contracts signed by 1972 amounted to 14 million tons of coal a year, although total Canadian production was only about 20,638,000 tons a year. Domestic demand for coal in 1972 was about 40 million tons (expected to rise to at least 55 million tons by 1980), of which half was imported from the United States (Table A.1). Clearly, output from Canada's coal mines will have to increase dramatically just to keep its 50 per cent share of Canada's market as well as meeting export commitments. The target set by the federal Department of Energy, Mines and Resources is 37 million tons a year by 1980, a goal which, if met, will still leave Canada heavily dependent on coal imports, mainly from the United States. Furthermore, the growing interest in gasification and liquefaction of coal to make synthetic natural gas and crude oil could further increase pressure on the Canadian coal industry. Reserves are not a limiting factor and should be adequate for a century or more (Table A.2); the problem is getting it out of the ground quickly without causing undue environmental damage.

Strip mining presents the biggest environmental problem for the coal industry: in prairie regions of Alberta and Saskatchewan, land reclamation and revegetation would add an estimated 2 per cent to the cost of the coal ($300 to $600 an acre of mined land),

FIGURE A1

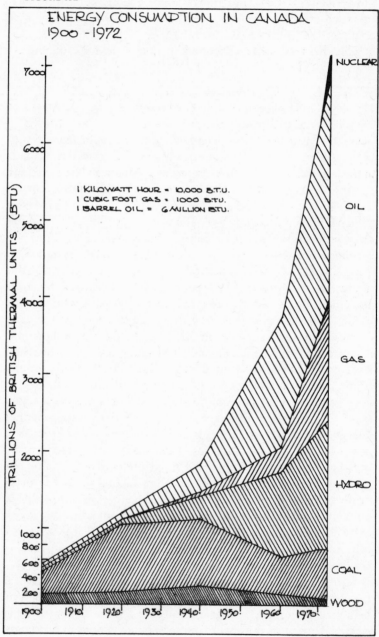

ENERGY CONSUMPTION IN CANADA
1900 - 1972

1 KILOWATT HOUR = 10,000 B.T.U.
1 CUBIC FOOT GAS = 1000 B.T.U.
1 BARREL OIL = 6 MILLION B.T.U.

FIGURE A2

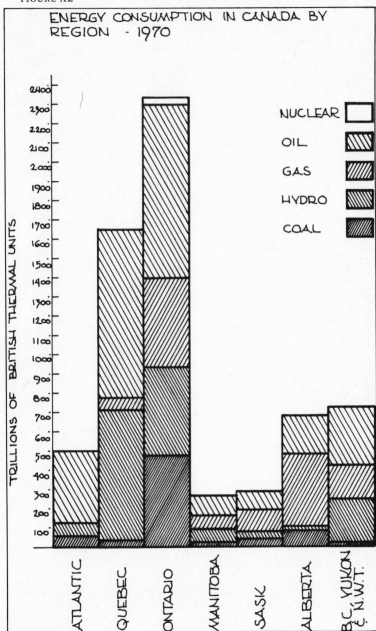

ENERGY CONSUMPTION IN CANADA BY REGION - 1970

NUCLEAR

OIL

GAS

HYDRO

COAL

FIGURE A3

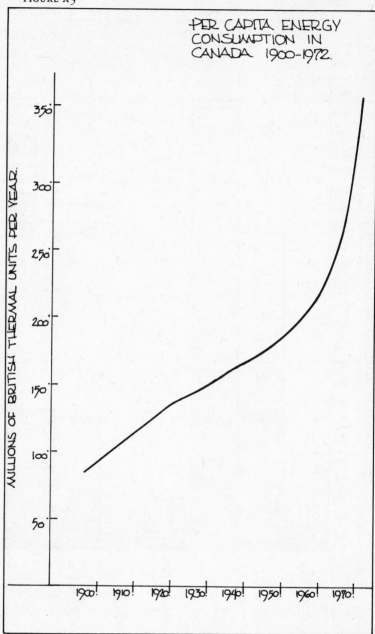

PER CAPITA ENERGY
CONSUMPTION IN
CANADA 1900-1972.

FIGURE A4

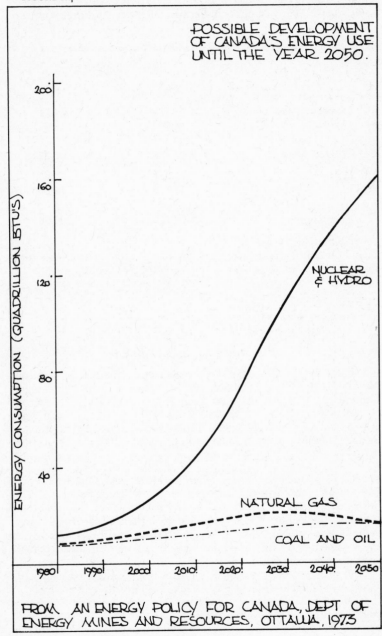

POSSIBLE DEVELOPMENT OF CANADA'S ENERGY USE UNTIL THE YEAR 2050.

ENERGY CONSUMPTION (QUADRILLION BTU'S)

NUCLEAR & HYDRO

NATURAL GAS

COAL AND OIL

FROM AN ENERGY POLICY FOR CANADA, DEPT OF ENERGY MINES AND RESOURCES, OTTAWA, 1973

but in mountainous regions of Alberta and British Columbia the costs soar to about 15 per cent because of the more difficult terrain.

TABLE A.1   COAL & COKE SUPPLY & DEMAND IN CANADA, 1962 & 1972

(in thousands of tons)

	1962	1972
Domestic demand	22,515	26,710
Exports (coal)	894	9,421
(coke)	131	263
Total demand	23,540	36,394
Production	10,217	20,638
Imports (coal)	12,322	18,569
(coke)	233	777
Total supply	22,772	39,984

SOURCE: Statistics Canada.
Note: Ontario currently accounts for nearly 90% of coal imports to Canada: all of the province's coal is supplied by U.S. mines.

TABLE A.2   CANADA'S COAL RESERVES
(thousands of tons)

Province	Measured	Indicated	Inferred	Total
Nova Scotia	126,000	466,000	684,000	1,276,000
New Brunswick	10,000	—	—	10,000
Ontario	240,000	—	—	240,000
Saskatchewan	291,500	7,024,000	4,698,400	12,013,900
Alberta	2,203,900	32,096,100	12,940,200	47,240,200
British Columbia	7,328,600	11,175,400	40,953,000	59,457,000
Total	10,200,000	50,761,500	59,275,600	120,237,100

SOURCE: Department of Energy, Mines and Resources, Ottawa.
Notes: "Measured [proved] reserves" are those which have been demonstrated to exist by actual drilling and measurement. The computed tonnage is judged to be accurate within 20 per cent of the true tonnage.
    "Indicated [probable] reserves" are estimated partly by drilling and measurement and partly by projecting known data to areas where there is an assumed continuity.
    "Inferred [possible] reserves" are estimated by educated guesswork based on a broad knowledge of the geology of an area or deposit.
    Coal is known to exist in Canada's north as well, but no estimate of northern reserves has ever been made.

In eastern Canada, the coal industry is under government control, but in the west production facilities are becoming concentrated in disturbingly few hands: eight companies accounted for 90 per cent of the region's coal production in 1972, and four of these companies are U.S.-controlled (Table A.3). The trend toward foreign ownership can be expected to continue in the absence of government action, as multinational oil companies seek to diversify their interests by investing in alternative energy sources like coal and uranium.

TABLE A.3   FOREIGN OWNERSHIP AND CONTROL
            IN THE CANADIAN ENERGY INDUSTRY

Industry	Assets ($ million)	Percentage non-resident-owned*	Percentage non-resident-controlled*
Electrical industry	15,966	3.5	1.0
Petroleum (oil and gas)	10,725	76.8	91.3
Petroleum transport (basically pipelines)	4,108	21.8	18.7
Coal mining	n.a.	60.3	73.2
Uranium	n.a.	24.3	22.5

SOURCE: *An Energy Policy for Canada*, Department of Energy, Mines and Resources, Ottawa, 1973.
* "Non-resident ownership" is the percentage of total assets in the industry owned by non-residents. "Non-resident control" is the percentage of total assets which come under the control of non-residents through non-resident ownership of over 50 per cent of the equity capital of a firm.

ELECTRICITY

Use of electricity in Canada is increasing even more rapidly than the average for all energy: at an average annual rate of 6.7 per cent, for a doubling time of about nine years. Electricity demand is expected to jump from 202.3 billion kilowatt-hours in 1970, to 396 billion kilowatt-hours in 1980, to 1,132 billion kilowatt-hours by 2000. In 1940, domestic electricity consumption was only 40 billion kilowatt-hours. Only Norway uses more electrical energy per capita than Canada: the United States, Sweden and Luxembourg rank third, fourth and fifth respectively in per capita electricity consumption. Production patterns within the industry are changing: between 1945 and 1972 hydro's share of total electricity generation dropped from 97.6 per cent to 75.1 per cent, while thermal generation jumped from 2.4 to 22.1 per cent. Nuclear power accounted for 2.8 per cent of the total in 1972 (Figures A.5 and A.6).

The electricity market is currently divided this way: 24 per cent residential, 16 per cent commercial and 60 per cent industrial.

About three-quarters of Canada's electrical energy is currently provided by hydroelectric developments. However, following completion of projects currently under construction in Manitoba, Quebec and British Columbia, it is unlikely that hydroelectric generation will maintain its historical growth rate. Undeveloped hydro sites near load centres are scarce, and the high cost of transmission lines from remote sites makes it increasingly difficult for hydro to compete economically with nuclear and other thermal power. And as resistance to the James Bay project in Quebec and the Churchill River diversion in Manitoba have shown, environmental constraints will come increasingly into play in the future. Thus, the portion of the estimated 60,000 to 85,000 megawatts of undeveloped hydro potential remaining in the country that will be developed within the foreseeable future will likely be small.

In 1970 fixed assets belonging to electric utilities in Canada amounted to $16 billion; capital investment by the utilities in that year were $1.6 billion—15 per cent of total business capital expenditure. To keep up with domestic demand for electricity, doubling every nine years, the industry must invest $16 billion over the years 1970 to 1979, $32 billion between 1979 and 1988, $64 billion over the following nine years, and so on. This, rather than any shortage of energy-producing resources, is the main problem facing the electrical utilities in Canada. (In fact, capital expenditures will probably be even higher, since nuclear power stations trade off high initial capital costs, as compared with other thermal generating facilities, against very low fuel costs. Total investment in nuclear power in Canada by 2000 is expected to be about $50 billion.)

OIL

The oil and gas boom experienced in Canada beginning in the early 1950s was part of a world-wide phenomenon brought about mainly by the development of efficient, automatic oil burners for

TABLE A.4   CANADA'S GAS AND OIL RESOURCES

	In place	Recoverable	Cumulative production	Remaining
Proved oil reserves (billion barrels)				
NWT	0.5	0.1	0.1	0.1
W. Canada	43.8	15.9	6.2	9.7
E. Canada	0.2	0.1	0.1	0.1
Proved natural gas reserves (trillion cu. ft.)				
NWT	2.0	1.3	—	1.3
W. Canada	116.5	69.1	17.8	51.4
E. Canada	1.1	1.0	0.7	0.3

SOURCE: Canadian Petroleum Association, 1972.

Potential oil reserves (billion barrels)

Arctic Islands and NWT	28.1
W. Canada (provinces)	4.6
East coast offshore	50.4

Potential natural gas reserves (trillion cu. ft.)

Arctic Islands and NWT	341.7
W. Canada (provinces)	43.7
East coast offshore	326.1

SOURCE: Geological Survey of Canada, 1973.

Alberta tar sands (billion barrels)

Proved recoverable	26.5
Ultimate recoverable	250

SOURCE: Alberta Energy Resources Conservation Board, 1972.
Notes: "Proved reserves" are those which can be demonstrated with reasonable certainty to be recoverable under existing economic and technological conditions.

"Potential reserves" as measured by the Geological Survey of Canada have an estimated 50/50 probability of being recoverable in the stated amounts. There is a decreasing probability of recovering more, and an increasing probability of recovering less. These predictions are highly speculative and may vary widely depending on the surveyor.

"In place" reserve is the amount of oil or gas originally in place within a field, part of which is recoverable and part of which cannot be recovered.

"Remaining" reserve is the recoverable reserve minus the cumulative production to date.

---

domestic heating. The growth in size, weight and horsepower of the American automobile, the growth in the trucking and airline industries and conversion of the railways from steam to diesel-electric added extra impetus to the strongly surging demand. Production in Canada expanded rapidly until 1959, when the United States imposed import quotas on Canadian oil; by 1962 competition from cheap foreign crude would virtually have ended growth but for a federal government decision in 1961 to establish a national oil policy, under which that part of the country lying west of the Ottawa Valley was to be supplied exclusively by oil from western Canada, while territory east of the line would continue to rely on imported crude (mainly from South America). The Arab oil boycott and a new desire for self-sufficiency of supplies led Ottawa in 1974 to announce extension of the east-west pipeline system into the Montreal market, and there have been further calls for pipelines from Montreal into the Maritime provinces as well.

Oil exports from Canada first exceeded imports in 1969 (Table A.5), and by 1972 the industry had established a trade surplus of $334 million compared with a deficit of $174 million ten years earlier. Production comes almost entirely from the three western provinces, which account for about 75 per cent of total output.

Canada's proved reserves of oil are less than 10 billion barrels (not counting the 26.5 billion barrels of Athabasca tar sand oil classified as proved by the Alberta government) and the ratio of proved reserves to annual production is declining—from 24.5 in 1966 to 15 in 1972. (In the same period the ratio in the United States declined from 7.2 to 6.0.) For several years production from western oil fields has been at or near full capacity (as opposed to 50 per cent in the mid 1960s). The upward curve of oil production from the western provinces is thus expected to level off by the late 1970s, and then fall into a decline.

TABLE A.5   OIL SUPPLY AND DEMAND IN CANADA 1955-1972*
(thousands of barrels per day)

	1955	1965	1970	1972	Average annual growth %
Production	360	923	1,476	1,819	10.0
Imports	341	558	762	899	5.9
Total supply	701	1,481	2,239	2,718	8.3
Domestic demand	645	1,145	1,466	1,589	5.4
Exports	49	325	763	1,144	20.0
Total demand	694	1,470	2,229	2,733	8.4

SOURCE: Statistics Canada.
*Includes refined products.

Untapped reserves in the Alberta tar sands, in the Arctic and perhaps off Canada's east coast are abundant in terms of domestic demand, but the costs of transporting oil from frontier areas and of extracting oil from the tar sands will be immense: once again the size of the required capital expenditure seems to be the chief constraint in providing ample supplies for the future. Prudent domestic policy would seem to demand an end to oil exports to the United States in the very near future (modest export controls were imposed in 1973), although the two-price system for oil established by Ottawa early in 1974 makes revenues from export sales extremely attractive in the short run.

The oil industry in Canada is completely dominated by foreign-owned firms (Table A.3), with over four-fifths of exploration and production capacity and virtually all refining capacity in non-Canadian hands. The five largest oil companies in Canada are Imperial Oil (Exxon), Texaco, Mobil, Gulf and Shell; together they account for about 50 per cent of oil production, four-fifths of refining capacity and two-thirds of oil imports. Vertical integration in these firms gives them a high degree of immunity to government attempts to influence market conditions.

GAS

Production of natural gas in Canada has increased even more rapidly than that of oil, with an annual average growth rate of

FIGURE A5

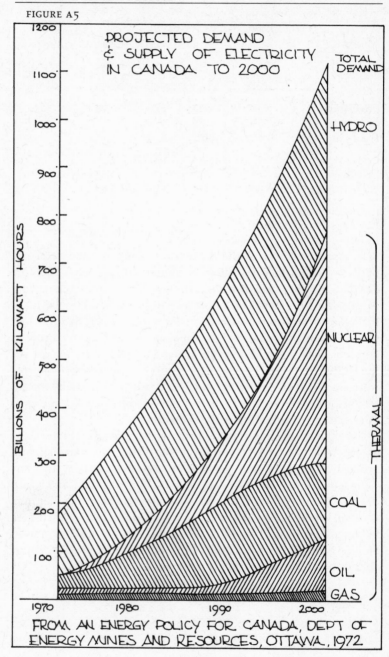

PROJECTED DEMAND & SUPPLY OF ELECTRICITY IN CANADA TO 2000

FROM AN ENERGY POLICY FOR CANADA, DEPT OF ENERGY MINES AND RESOURCES, OTTAWA, 1972

FIGURE A6

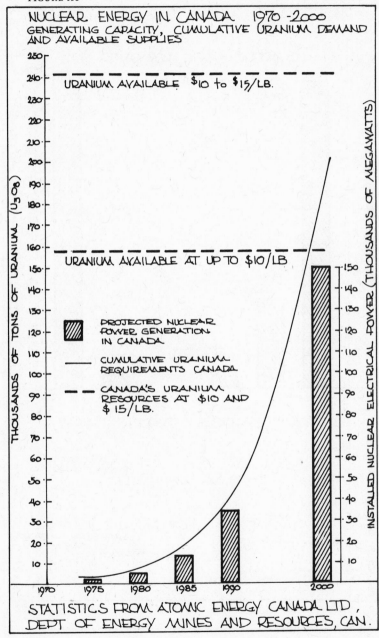

NUCLEAR ENERGY IN CANADA 1970-2000
GENERATING CAPACITY, CUMULATIVE URANIUM DEMAND
AND AVAILABLE SUPPLIES

URANIUM AVAILABLE $10 to $15/LB.

URANIUM AVAILABLE AT UP TO $10/LB

PROJECTED NUCLEAR
POWER GENERATION
IN CANADA

CUMULATIVE URANIUM
REQUIREMENTS CANADA

CANADA'S URANIUM
RESOURCES AT $10 AND
$15/LB.

THOUSANDS OF TONS OF URANIUM (U₃O₈)

INSTALLED NUCLEAR ELECTRICAL POWER (THOUSANDS OF MEGAWATTS)

STATISTICS FROM ATOMIC ENERGY CANADA LTD,
DEPT OF ENERGY MINES AND RESOURCES, CAN.

FIGURE A7

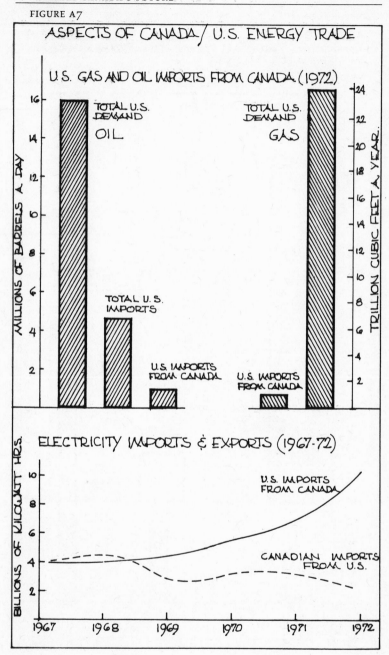

FIGURE A8

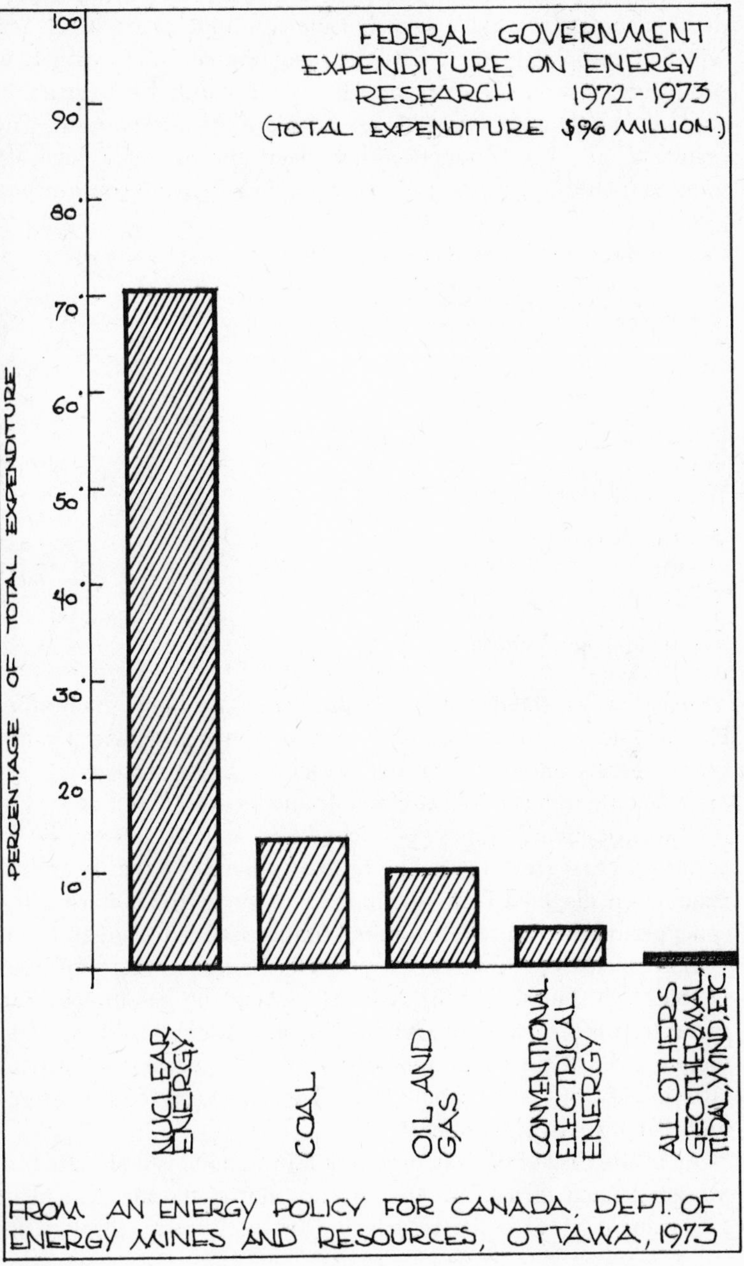

FEDERAL GOVERNMENT
EXPENDITURE ON ENERGY
RESEARCH   1972 - 1973
(TOTAL EXPENDITURE $96 MILLION)

PERCENTAGE OF TOTAL EXPENDITURE

NUCLEAR ENERGY.

COAL

OIL AND GAS

CONVENTIONAL ELECTRICAL ENERGY

ALL OTHERS GEOTHERMAL TIDAL, WIND, ETC.

FROM AN ENERGY POLICY FOR CANADA, DEPT. OF
ENERGY MINES AND RESOURCES, OTTAWA, 1973

nearly 19 per cent (Table A.6). As in the case of oil, most production comes from the western provinces. Imports are small, and will end completely by 1976 when existing contracts with U.S. producers expire. Exports, on the other hand, have virtually exploded at an annual growth rate of more than 30 per cent. The result of all this production has been that Canada faces an imminent shortage of natural gas, assuming demand continues to

TABLE A.6   NATURAL GAS SUPPLY AND DEMAND IN CANADA 1955-1972
(billions of cubic feet)

	1955	1965	1970	1972	Average annual growth %
Production	123	1,107	1,839	2,252	18.7
Imports	11	45	11	16	
Total supply	134	1,152	1,850	2,268	18.1
Domestic demand	124	631	1,044	1,256	14.5
Exports	11	404	780	1,012	30.4
Total demand	135	1,035	1,824	2,268	18.1

SOURCE: Statistics Canada.

increase as projected. Export commitments are huge, amounting by 1974 to 15 trillion cubic feet over the subsequent twenty years—nearly one-third of proved reserves. These proved reserves are adequate to meet domestic requirements until about 1985, but the added demand from export contracts reduces reserve life to about six years from 1974. The ratio of proved reserves to annual production declined from 39 in 1962 to 23 in 1972: during the same period the ratio in the United States declined from 20 to 11.

Gas reserves in Canada's Arctic are thought to be enormous (Table A.4), but so are the costs of getting the gas to southern markets. Once again, prudent domestic policy would seem to dictate a sharp cut-back in exports to the United States, particularly in view of the extremely low price being received for the gas under many existing contracts.

As in the case of oil, gas production in Canada is dominated by foreign-owned firms. In the Arctic, however, the Canadian government plays a major role in gas exploration through its controlling interest in Panarctic Oils Limited, a consortium which has been responsible for a number of major gas finds in recent years.

Selected Bibliography

BOOKS

Canada Year Book. Ottawa: Information Canada, various years.

M. A. CARRIGY and J. W. KRAMER. *Guide to the Athabasca Oil Sands Area.* Edmonton: Alberta Research, 1973.

Conservation and Utilization Committee. *Fort McMurray Athabasca Tar Sands Development Strategy.* Edmonton: Study prepared for the Alberta Government, 1972.

RICHARD CURTIS and ELIZABETH HOGAN. *Perils of the Peaceful Atom.* New York: Ballantine Books, 1970.

T. K. DERRY and TREVOR I. WILLIAMS. *A Short History of Technology.* London: Oxford University Press, 1960.

WILFRED EGGLESTON. *Canada's Nuclear Story.* Toronto: Clarke Irwin, 1965.

An Energy Policy for Canada. Vols. I and II. Ottawa: Information Canada, 1973.

An Environmental Study of the Athabasca Tar Sands. Edmonton: Alberta Department of the Environment, 1973.

R. C. FITZSIMMONS. *The Truth about the Alberta Tar Sands.* Edmonton: privately printed, 1953.

JOHN HOLDREN and PHILIP HERRARA. *Energy.* California: Sierra Club, 1971.

H. H. LANSBERG, L. L. FISCHMAN and J. L. FISHER. *Resources in America's Future.* Baltimore: Johns Hopkins Press, 1963.

J. W. MACNEILL. *Environmental Management.* Ottawa: Information Canada, 1971.

JUDITH MAXWELL. *Energy from the Arctic: Facts and Issues.* Ottawa: Canadian-American Committee, 1973.

D. L. MEADOWS, *et al*. *The Limits to Growth*. M.I.T.–Club of Rome, 1972.

DOUGLAS PIMLOTT, *et al*. *Arctic Alternatives*. Ottawa: Canadian Arctic Resources Committee, 1973.

WADE ROWLAND. *The Plot to Save the World*. Toronto: Clarke Irwin, 1973.

———— and TINY BENNETT. *The Pollution Guide*. Toronto: Clarke Irwin, 1972.

PHILIP SYKES. *Sellout*. Edmonton: Hurtig, 1973.

PETER J. USHER and GRAHAME BEAKHURST. *Land Regulation in the Canadian North*. Ottawa: Canadian Arctic Resources Committee, 1973.

MASON ULLRICH, ed. *Civilian Nuclear Power and Internal Security*. New York: Praeger, 1971.

ARTICLES

HANNES ALFVEN. "Fission Energy and Other Sources of Energy." *Science and Public Affairs*, January 1974.

Atomic Energy of Canada Limited:
Annual Reports to 1973

    G. L. BROOKS, "Power Reactor Types." Nuclear Symposium Series

    W. M. CAMPBELL, "The Future World Energy Situation and Its Technical Implications"

    ————, "The Management of Radioactive By-products from a Nuclear Power Plant"

    L. R. HAYWOOD, "The Differences Between CANDU and Other Steam Generating Facilities"

    G. C. LAURENCE, "Nuclear Power Station Safety in Canada"

    L. PEASE, "Licencing Nuclear Power Stations in Canada," Nuclear Symposium Series

    G. A. PON, "The Fundamentals of Nuclear Power," Nuclear Symposium Series

    Report of the Waste Management Committee

    J. D. SAINSBURY, "Accident Analysis," Nuclear Symposium Series

R. STEPHEN BERRY and MARGARET F. FELS. "The Energy Cost of Automobiles." *Science and Public Affairs*, vol. 24, no. 10, December 1973.

G. C. BUTLER. "Health Hazards from Nuclear Sources." Ottawa: National Research Council of Canada.

Canadian Arctic Gas Study Limited. "How Gas Shortages Can Be Avoided in Canada," December 22, 1973.

Canadian Arctic Gas Study Limited. "Why Canada Needs the Arctic Pipeline," October 3, 1973.

HERMAN E. DALY. "The Stationary-State Economy." *Ecologist*, vol. 2, no. 7, July 1972.

JOEL DATMSTADTER. "Limiting the Demand for Energy." *Environmental Affairs*, vol. 1, no. 2, 1973.

GISELDA DRESCHHOFF, D. F. SAUNDERS and E. J. ZELLER. "International High Level Nuclear Waste Management." *Science and Public Affairs*, January 1974.

RICHARD N. GOODWIN. "Reflections: The American Condition." *New Yorker*, January 21, 28, February 3, 1974.

ERIC HIRST. "Transportation Energy Use and Conservation Potential." *Science and Public Affairs*, vol. 29, no. 9, November 1973.

M. K. HUBBERT. "The Energy Resources of the Earth." *Scientific American*, 225, 1971.

ERIC KIERANS. "The Day the Cabinet Was Misled." *Canadian Forum*, March 1974.

ARTHUR S. KUBO and DAVID J. ROSE. "Disposal of Nuclear Wastes." *Science*, vol. 182, no. 4118, December 21, 1973.

IRVING LIKE. "Tuning Down the GNP." *Environment*, vol. 15, no. 6, August 1973.

L. G. MCCONNELL. "Construction and Operating Experience with Thermal Power Reactors in Canada." Toronto: Ontario Hydro.

JOHN MCPHEE. "The Curve of Binding Energy" (Theodore B. Taylor Profile). *New Yorker*, December 3, 10 and 17, 1973.

"Northern Exploration Report." *Oilweek*, vol. 25, no. 3, March 4, 1974.

Northern Perspectives. Ottawa: Canadian Arctic Resources Committee: monthly, vol. 1, no. 1, to vol. 2, no. 1, January 1974.

SHELDON NOVICK. "Looking Forward." *Environment*, vol. 15, no. 4, May 1973.

Ontario Ministry of the Environment. "Effects of Thermal Pollution."

ROBERT PAGE, *et al.* "Energy Sell-Out." *Canadian Forum*, June-July, 1973.

WALTER C. PATTERSON. "The British Atom." *Environment*, vol. 14, no. 10, 1972.

MICHAEL J. PERELMAN. "Farming with Petroleum." *Environment*, vol. 14, no. 8, October 1972.

T. B. REED and R. M. LERNER. "Methanol: A Versatile Fuel for Immediate Use." *Science*, vol. 182, no. 4119, December 28, 1973.

MALCOLM SLERRER. "Energy Analysis in Policy Making." *New Scientist*, November 1, 1973.

RICHARD G. STEIN. "A Matter of Design." *Environment*, vol. 14, no. 8, October 1974.

United States Development Agency Yearbook of Agriculture.

LOWELL WOOD and JOHN NUCKOLLS. "Fusion Power." *Environment*, vol. 14, no. 4, May 1972.